W0008356

Fed UP!

An Illustrated Guide
to
Food Freedom

Spoiler Alert:
It's NOT about the Food!

Written & Illustrated by
Katie Barbaro

Published by Orchard Press, LLC
Copyright 2021 by Katie Barbaro
All rights reserved.

Library of Congress Cataloging-in-Publication Data

Barbaro, Katie
FED UP - An Illustrated Guide to Food Freedom
ISBN: 978-0-9882451-8-1

The Kitchen Table of Contents

Welcome to our CookBook!

It's time to Pre-Heat the (L)oven!

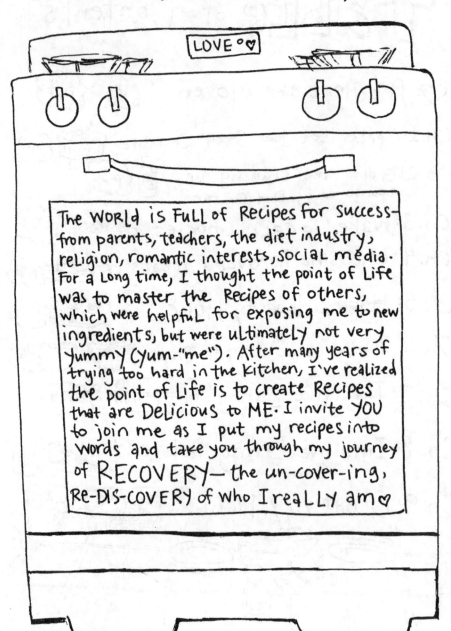

LOVE °♥

The WORLD is FuLL of Recipes for success—from parents, teachers, the diet industry, religion, romantic interests, social media. For a Long time, I thought the point of Life was to master the Recipes of others, which were helpful for exposing me to new ingredients, but were ultimately not very yummy (yum-"me"). After many years of trying too hard in the kitchen, I've realized the point of Life is to create Recipes that are Delicious to ME. I invite YOU to join me as I put my recipes into words and take you through my journey of RECOVERY— the un-cover-ing, RE-DIS-COVERY of who I really am ♥

What does "FOOD FREEDOM" mean?

Before finding recovery, I was locked up in an invisible cage of food & body obsession — counting calories, eating sneakily, bingeing & purging, over-exercising, under-carbing, trying to control my life by controlling my food. The most debilitating part of disordered eating was the SECRECY behind it. On the outside, I was a "successful" occupational therapist, improviser, girlfriend, but on the inside I was maniacally calculating my every caloric move, living in a prison of isolation. I am sharing my haphazard journey of recovery in hopes it might make someone else feel less alone on the path to FREEDOM ♡

What does it mean to be Fed UP?

It means I find puns irresistable.

I'm FED UP with believing I should be something I'm not.

I'm FED UP with DIETING

I'm FED UP with fearing fatness.

I'm FED UP with the OPPRESSION of people in Larger Bodies, AND with the oppression of people PERIOD- of any size, gender, color, ethnicity, sexual orientation, etc.

I'm FED UP with CONDITIONALLY loving my Body.

I'm FED UP with PRETENDING to be FINE

I'm FED UP with tying my worthiness to NUMBERS [Weight, BMI, calories in/out]

I'm FED UP with waiting until I'm "ready" to share my story with the WORLD.

I'm FED UP with being FED UP and NOT doing anything about it♡

Who is that? →

Hi! I'm Katie! You will see me throughout this book talking to future-me or past-me or talking to present-me from the future or past, often saying things I've thought in my head but haven't said with my mouth. You may feel like you're reading my diary, which you have my enthusiastic PERMISSION to do!

I've thought a lot about how I'd like to have more diversity in my characters—size, shape, gender, hair style, clothing taste. I want to invite everyBODY to see their BODY here!......But then I realized I am sharing how I process my experience of living in a human body. I could never insert YOU into my story because you have your own unique story (that I hope you share in your own unique way)♡ So although my cartoons are all vaguely "me"-looking, I intend to liberate all Bodies & Beings, not just the ones that look like me♡

Note to the Reader:

 It tickles me that I am writing these words NOW and you are also reading them NOW. I feel excited to be sharing my inside thoughts with you in this moment — the present moment we're both inside of. In this way, all books are portals, allowing us to meet in a place that transcends time and space. I love thinking about this stuff.

As I write this, I am reminded that I am always exactly where I'm meant to be (we all are...even when it doesn't feel that way...I certainly don't always feel this way) and right now we get to be on the same page at the same time! It feels special!!

Thank you for being here on this page with me. I invite you to spend even more "heres" & "Nows" with me as we embark on this journey together. Without any further ado, here we go! ♡

Chapter 1
Apple "Let Your Story" Crumble

6 apples (stories from your life), diced +

1 stick of Cold Butter (LOVE) + 1½ cups flour (FEAR)

mix til it looks like sand, then add:
♡ 2 tsp. cinnamon
♡ ½ cup sugar
♡ ½ cup oats

1 Tbsp Sugar (sweet memories) + 2 Tbsp Cinnamon (spicy memories)

1. Admit you are crumbling inside
2. Toss your juicy apple bits in a pan
3. Top with your crumbly bits
4. Let it cook as long as it needs to (30 mins @ 375°F)
5. Let it cool, slap a slab of ice cream (COURAGE) on top and Enjoy as the crumbliest bits of you become the yumminess they were always meant to be.

Your life is Delicious!

Here's a slice of mine....

This ominous peach warning is burned in my Brain from my mom's diet book in the bathroom drawer, which I sneakily devoured as soon as I could read. I felt like I was unearthing the Secrets of the Universe that the grown-ups were afraid to tell me — and in a way, I WAS. The subtle, toxic imprint of diet culture was taking hold of my subconscious mind as I sat there on the toilet fantasizing about eating nothing but cucumbers when I grew up.

Fun Fact: Kids don't do what you say, they do what you DO.

My parents were (are) so so so Loving, generous, & supportive. I do not want to blame them in any way, but I DO want to illuminate the sneakiness of how generational trauma, subconscious limiting beliefs, and fear-based societal brainwashing get transmitted.

Seeing my mom constantly dieting & trying to change her body made me feel like I should be doing that too. No matter how many times she reassured me I "wasn't fat," I couldn't shake the uncomfortable reality of "feeling fat." We were both sinking (hoping to be shrinking) in a giant pool of Fat Phobic quicksand.

↳more on Fatphobia soon!

Despite "feeling fat" for most of my life, I have lived in a body that the world deems "normal-sized." I live with "Thin Privilege" in a world where people in larger bodies are systemically discriminated against, bullied, and abused. Though I have never been the direct target of such attacks, my internalized fear of fatness was running the show. I always felt "wrong-sized," like a stranger in my own home, convinced that my double chin and underarm fat were the source of all my problems.

My subconscious brain receptors were constantly on the lookout for evidence that my body was too big. When I was eight, I cried to my mom because I was twice the size of my same-aged cousin. In high school, a costume fitter remarked, "You have Birthing Hips... it's a good thing!" It did NOT feel like a good thing to me. (I can imagine this comment might feel good if I were seconds away from giving birth.)

Recently, I asked my mom what her Biggest Disappointment in Life has been. Without missing a beat, she said,

My Looks.

The honesty & simplicity of her answer hit me like a sack of Bricks, which I caught and held onto with the outward expression, "We're cool! Everything's fine!" and the inward knowing, "THIS is exactly why I want to write this BOOK."

Emotional BRICKS

Now that I've had a chance to unpack the sack and lay out the bricks, I can see the foundation my house was built on. It's not a surprise, but it's a shockingly clear message about the lies I'm here to DISMANTLE — not just for myself, but for all people who do not feel at home in their bodies, who believe they should look different than they do.

We are exactly WHERE we are meant to be, HOW we are meant to be here.

I know in my BONES this is true, but it's not a constant, indelible state of knowing...

It is a remembering and forgetting that flows in and out. Adjusting to the flow can feel destabilizing at first, but eventually a calmness settles in with each wave.

... So what I'm hearing you say is:

1. You kind of believe in me, but not really.

2. Keep my clothes on (very happy to adopt this one).

3. If I lose weight I will be a wildly successful actress— No one will have to tell me to get smaller because I'll already be the right size! (This must be why I see you diet all the time too!)

Note to Brain: File this Post-it under "career goals"

Hearing my parents' reaction to my dream of being an actress was a similar "A ha" moment to finding the diet book in the bathroom. I had discovered the secret to success: Losing weight!

16

The only Problem was...
I Knew I wouldn't be allowed
to go on a diet. Ugh!

Thankfully my obedience to my parents
was stronger than my emerging hatred
of my body.
But I still
tucked away
the goal of
under eating and
over exercising.

"Someday" came one summer night when I was between my two years of Grad School getting my Occupational Therapy degree (AKA following the "Back-Up Plan" protocol, which ended up being exactly what I was meant to do at the time, as all things are). I was sitting on the couch watching "The Biggest Loser" with my parents—a TV show where contestants get shipped off to an isolated farm-like setting and bullied into drastically changing their diet & exercise routines. We were watching the finale where the final contestants were weighing in. (I hadn't been following the show, but "The Biggest Loser" was the only program on my parents' DVR queue deemed (by me) Fun for the Whole Family.

ALL Recordings

▶ ⏺ ⏹ 97% Full (of Shit)

📁 Judge Judy

📁 Hallmark Movies

📁 Misc. Propaganda

The Biggest Loser (53 mins)

Watch as contestants develop (even more) disordered relationships with food and their bodies in the elusive quest for lasting "healthy" weight loss. Toxic Fun for The Whole Family!

On her final Weigh-in, one of the women

Weighed **My Dream Weight**

the Weight I had Lied about when I was filling out my Driver's License Application in High School.

If this Lady can Lose half her body mass & weigh what I've been pretending to weigh for years, surely I can get there with a little focused effort!

I mustered up the humility to ask for **help** from my Personal Trainer Little Brother, who had gone through a personal transformation himself, from being "overweight" as a kid (I was SO JEALOUS he got to go to "health" & "weight-loss" seminars with my mom) to becoming a ripped, *award-winning* body builder & personal Trainer.

"HELP" felt like a Literal & figurative FOUR LETTER WORD to me.

How do you *actually* Lose Weight??

My sweet little brother sat me down and introduced me to the *Magical World* of...

My Fatphobia PaL

How little can you get away with eating today?

Breakfast: Sad oats & egg whites

Snack 1: water & air

Lunch: chicken & a Run

Snack 2: drink your own tears

I started Religiously tracking & planning my daily meals on a diet app. I wasn't new to calorie counting, but this was the first time I felt confident going into my calorie restriction with a plan and someone (my little brother) to blame if it didn't work. My Lifelong Dream of losing weight finally felt within reach.

AND it sounded so HEaLthy. More mindfulness around what I was putting in my body sounded great. I was more motivated to exercise and even signed up for a half-marathon despite my lifelong career of HATING RUNNING.

💡 Suddenly, this area of life (food, body, "wellness," "fitness") that had always eluded & mystified me became CLEARER, more MANAGEABLE, under my CONTROL. (cue ominous music)

When I started losing weight, I was

*♥ BLISSED OUT *♥

Was there a greater high than this?

The ease & Lightness I felt in my body

The strength I felt performing new physical challenges

The newfound Sticktoitiveness I had unearthed in myself

SO MANY Compliments

Life could be SO easy if I turned it all into a math equation!

Four months after my dieting journey began, I ran a half marathon & felt like I was on top of the world! But soon after, the Spiritual Awakening-like highs I'd been reaching began to plateau. The number on the scale was stabilizing at my "dream weight," which no longer felt dreamy enough. The compliments on my appearance faded as people got used to this simply being what I looked like now.

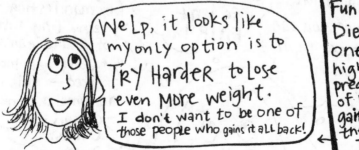

Fun Fact: Dieting is one of the highest predictors of weight gain in the Long-Term

I used to wake up every morning, workout, go to the bathroom (hopefully #2!) and **Weigh myself.**

If the number was...

Higher than yesterday, I would blame myself.

The **same** as yesterday, I felt betrayed.

Lower than yesterday, I felt cautiously celebratory.

This is what happens when you eat Pretzels, YOU GLUTTON!

For dinner, you can have Greek yogurt and a workout class.

What!? All of my hard work for NOTHING?! Life isn't FAIR!!

Yay! This is <u>so</u> WORTH IT! You're on your way to manifesting the teeny tiny life of your dreams! But don't get too excited — this is no time to think you can eat carbs.

The Pendulum Swing of Dieting Doom

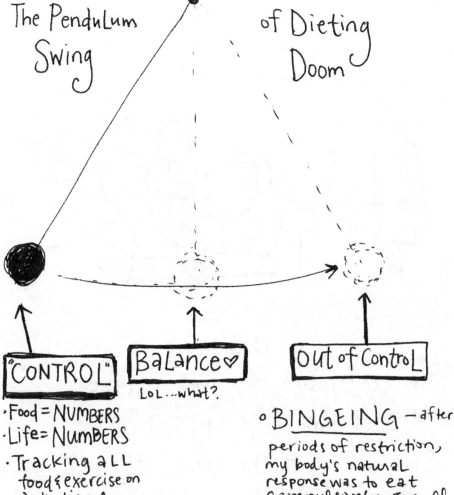

"CONTROL"
LoL...what?

- Food = NUMBERS
- Life = NUMBERS
- Tracking aLL food & exercise on a dieting App
- Weighing & measuring everything I put in my body
- Exercising compulsively At least once a day
- Obsessively calculating how much I had eaten, was "aLLowed" to eat later; and how much exercising I'd need to do to "Work it off."

BaLance ♡

Out of Control

- BINGEING – after periods of restriction, my body's natural response was to eat compulsively. I would take a bite (or 10) out of everything in the fridge, eat my roommates' food, which I'd replace secretly after eating the new package down to the correct level so as to go undetected (yeah right).

I was always PROUd of MYSelf for restricting my food intake and Ashamed of MYSeLf for succumbing to the temptation of food I'd actually enjoy.

The "high" I felt when I was <u>in</u> cOntroL had an equal & opposite "LOW" when I was <u>Out</u> of cOntroL.

My shame around Bingeing Kept me quiet about it, hoping it would go away on it's own.

I remember one weekend night in Grad school a few weeks after my half marathon...

80% of my self-allotted calorie intake for the day had been Coors Light Beers & protein bars and I drunkenly decided to allow myself

to EAT *a few bites of* my Boyfriend's Chipotle Burrito.

I asked...

This felt like radical & unprecedented self-permission-giving♡

Could you please order the salsa I don't like on the side? I'm gonna have a few bites!

Grad Student with Honors

This is **NOT** a dramatization. I wept uncontrollably for at least an hour, as the sweet, hungry, eager child inside of me had gotten her hopes up for finally getting the 3 bites of burrito she'd been longing for, only to find those bites would be slathered in spicy salsa, rendering them completely

Unpalatable.

Hey! I'm your palate, and frankly I find everything about this whole dieting thing to be "unpalatable."

My Boyfriend – let's call him Ronald – reacted in the most supportive way he could muster after being accused of

RUINING my Life.

I know what you're thinking...
(or at least I know what I think you're thinking)

WOW! The Burrito Incident of 2011 Sounds like the PERFECT Wake Up Call, Rock-Bottom-esque experience to help you see the UTTER INSANITY you were subjecting yourself to!

That would have been nice, but as you can see, this experience fit quite nicely into my meticulously designed formula for "How to do Life."

HOW TO DO LIFE

Eat Something "BAD" → Feel SAD ↘
Fix it with a Dieting FAD
Feel GLAD
Fix it with a Dieting FAD
Feel GLAD
Feel MAD ← Eat Something "BAD"

Now that's an accurate Dieting AD!

Chapter 2
"Guilt-Free" Crunchy Air

Sponsored by Diet Culture

1. Open a pack of Rice Cakes

2. Put one or two (if you've been "good") on a plate

3. Pretend to enjoy whilst feeling Dead Inside

SALT-FREE TASTE-FREE Rice Cakes

➪ One of my <u>Subconscious Beliefs</u>, dating back to my sitting-on-the-toilet-reading-Mom's-Diet-Book Days was

"Everybody Must think this way — especially all the hot people."

OR

"If someone feels good about their body it's only because they work very hard at fixing it... I must work harder!"

Hearing "I can eat carbs without hating myself" Made me think, "You Liar! It's so sad that you're hiding your true feelings."

I have since learned that internalized

Fatphobia

(n.) the fear/hatred of fat bodies, a form of ≡ weight stigma ≡ prevalent in the western world

was at the ROOT of most of my
SKEWED SUBCONSCIOUS BELIEFS,
including, but not limited to:

"I feel fat" was my interpretation of all bodily discomfort.

I was afraid of getting Bigger.

Any time I didn't get my way, I assumed it was because of my Appearance.

I (incorrectly) believed I was fat & hated my body because of that.

FATPHOBIA

✳ I would have told you I had NO PROBLEM with anyone else's fat body, it was just mine that didn't deserve to exist. I didn't realize my self-fat-shaming had implications for all people.

✳ My fear of fatness made sense, since people in larger bodies are often discriminated against.

Meanwhile, I was Lying in bed with an under-fed stomach growling, feeling proud of myself for not exceeding my daily calorie goal while scrolling through mouth-watering food porn photos on my "Food Gawker" app that turned me On more than any ACTUAL PORN ever has.

My first experience of wanting to stop eating compulsively and not being able to was...

The Great* Cereal Binge of 2012

← Jk, there was no bowl or spoon, just my bare hands diving straight into the BOX.

*NOT SO Great

°°CANNOT. STOP. EATING KASHI GO LEAN CEREAL.

3 servings! 4...5...6!? WHat do I Do?!?

A. KEEP GOING—today is now your unintentional "CHEAT DAY"

B. RUN 5 miLes to "make up for it"

C. STOP BUYING CEREAL because your lustful paLate cannot be trusted around readily-consumabLe foods that can be eaten by the handfuL.

D. ALL of the ABOVE

...plus caLL mom to cry about it...

On a conscious level, I believed nothing was wrong. Restricting, over-exercising, bingeing, and meticulously tracking these activities had become NORMAL.
Diet culture had hijacked my brain (AND my doctor's brain, leading her to further NORMALIZE my behavior).

Fun Fact ♡
From Future Me:

YOU know better than the **DSM-5** [Diagnostic & Statistical Manual of Mental Disorders, 5th Edition] about whether you have a disordered relationship with food and/or your body ♡

↳ I wish this sign had been hanging in my Doctor's office.

I was in Major denial about my own disordered eating because I didn't see myself as "sick enough" to need help. I thought I was crazy & not strong enough because I couldn't stick to my rigid, restrictive eating plan without inevitably BINGEING.

Dieting itself is a process of Gas Lighting* the Body's Nervous System,

Using an external set of rules to govern eating & exercize and overriding the Body's internal wisdom.

> You're not REALLY hungry. Try drinking water instead.

> I don't care if you're tired, we have to go to the gym after work.

> You're craving something salty? That sounds like a bad idea.

> We don't eat when we feel like it, we eat at 8am, 11am, 2pm, and 6pm — get with the program!

> Nothing tastes as good as being skinny on your trip to Hawaii will feel.

* GASLIGHT: (V) To psychologically manipulate someone into questioning their own SANITY.

I distinctly remember that trip to Hawaii. Ronald (same boyfriend) and I flew to Kauai, the most mind-blowingly beautiful island EVER. I had worked SO HArd to get ⸝Vacation Skinny⸝ so as to look unmistakeably BLissful in Facebook photos & Secure Ronald's eternal Love.

One night, we decided to stay in, order a pizza, & watch "The BacheLor." (we watched "The BacheLor" in paradise··· not to be confused with "The Bachelor in Paradise.") The onLy thing I Longed for more than being as Tiny as Possible was to be a "cool, chill Girlfriend," which meant throwing my diet out the window, drinking my weight in mojitos, and eating Pizza for Dinner.

I've worked very hard to become this cool & chill!

Eating a slice of pizza felt like eating Forbidden Fruit, and immediately opened up the Pandora's Box of all my repressed desires & fears...

Are you REALLY happy in this RELATIONSHIP??

You don't even LIKE "The Bachelor"!

You want to eat all the Pizza on the PLANET.

Pandora's [Pizza] Box

You fundamentally believe you are NOT WORTHY of LOVE!

The "Zoning out whilst uncontrollably bingeing" on cereal" feeling came back and before I knew it, I had eaten the entire (rest of the) pizza by myself while Ronald was sleeping.

Oh dear. This went beyond being upset about the numbers, I could feel the over-fullness of my belly and I needed to make it go away.

I wanted desperately to press "Control-Z," undo what I had done. I went to the bathroom & for the first time ever attempted to make myself throw up. It didn't work, which made me feel like even more of a failure.

The feeling of wanting to punish myself by throwing up scared me— burned itself in my memory, saying, "This is the wake up call you ordered!"

I eagerly pressed the "snooze" button, which I had done many times before. Events Like these felt like signals from my soul that something was not right, but my conscious mind was not ready to face the discomfort and pain that would surely come from opening my eyes fully. So, I snoozed, knowing deep down there was more to Life than dieting obsession.

Hey there, how are you doing? Yes YOU.

I've been doing a lot of the talking so far, but I want this to feel more like a conversation. On that last page, I got worried I might sound like I'm judging myself or you for hitting the snooze button on our **Lives**, so I want to clarify, even hitting "Snooze" is an example of us doing the exact right thing at the exact right time.

Ram Dass talks about how going back to SLEEP is part of the AWAKENING process.

"You have to stand back one step further and see your whole Life, The Awakening and the Going to Sleep, ALL as Awakening... allow the dance to go on UP and down, UP and down."
— Ram Dass

♡ I find this to be comforting and true ♡

For me, the illusion created by Diet Culture made it pretty freakin' easy to "go back to sleep."
It felt comforting to operate within a system of good/bad, Right/Wrong.

Today I ate only good foods, no bad foods, and I exercised, which is good! I'm such a good person!

As a natural fan of sticker charts and other external measures of success, dieting was highly gratifying for me.

Daily Progress Report*

I weigh under XXX lbs ☆

I ate under XXXX cals ☆

I worked out for xx hours ☆

I loved myself ~~un~~conditionally ☆

I looked in the mirror without cringing ☆

Team Meeting

Living according to the rules & ideals of Diet Culture (and other external value systems) made my mind, body & heart feel ~~disjointed~~ rather than aLigned.

My diet/body-obsessed mind was an abusive partner trying to control my body's every move. Naturally, my body was constantly looking for ways to fuel itself when my mind wasn't looking.

Yay! She's drunk! This is our chance to eat all the things we're Never allowed to eat!

↰The Night Before

The Morning After↘

How could you do this you big fat idiot?!

You're right, I was bad. How much do you want me to run this time?

AS Long as my Love or Respect for my body was CONDITIONAL upon how it Looked, how much it weighed, how many squats it could do **in a barre class**, there was a flavor of fear in the relationship.

Sometimes, my mind tried to run away from my body, fantasizing about divorcing her forever.

A psychologist might call this

Dissociation

I experienced it as out-of-control

Binge Eating ...

which was SCARY because I didn't want to be doing it, but I couldn't stop doing it.

NOW I can see how Binge Eating was an Adaptive Response...

My body was responding naturally to Biological & emotional FOOD DEPRIVATION. Even though I thought I was eating enough, I was not.

My body was attempting to anchor my dissociated mind with the grounding sensation of eating food.

My body was doing the correct protocol for being in starvation mode.

Thanks, Body!

Responses to Discomfort

There's a fine line between <u>identifying as</u> the highly judgmental mind and <u>being</u> a non-judgmental observer of the mind.

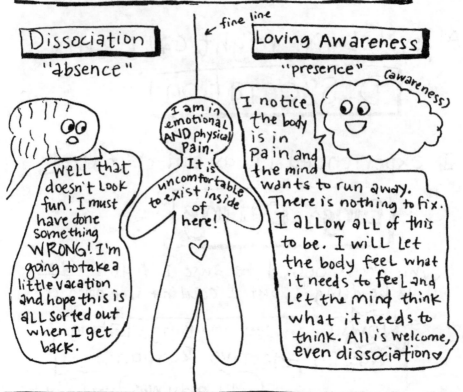

...of course I didn't know this at the time. I may have understood it intellectually from things I'd heard in psychology and yoga classes, but the wisdom was not integrated into my Body. My judgmental mind had me stuck in a loop of striving to be Fine.

Chapter 3
Wake Up Call
Cookies

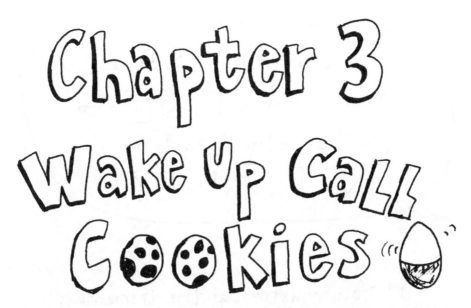

1. In clockwise order, add...

¼c. sugar
½c. brown sugar
½c. Butter

1 egg + 1 tsp vanilla

½tsp Baking soda
½tsp Salt

1 c. flour (¼c. at a time)

¾c. Chocolate chips

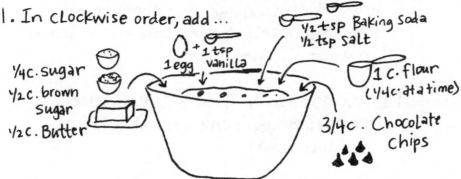

2. Eat half the batter straight from the bowl.

3. Place the remaining 3 cookies on a baking sheet & bake 10-13 minutes at 350°F.

4. Forget the cookies in the oven & return to a kitchen/Life engulfed in

FLAMES

Hey, Universe? How do I go from being "FINE" to finally admitting I'm NOT FINE?

☐ You muster up the tremendous amount of courage it takes to face yourself & the people & circumstances in your life honestly.

☐ You humbly ask for guidance, realizing you can't do everything on your own.

☐ You question thoughts & beliefs you have that are holding you back from being the you-est version of you.

This is the one I "chose" even though it didn't feel like a choice

☑ You hit a catastrophic ROCK BOTTOM that forces you to do ALL of the above steps for survival (and eventually THRIVAL♥)

Let me Set the Wake-Up Call Stage..

It was a hot Memorial Day Weekend & I had trekked from Los Angeles to an even hotter Arizona with Ronald and our friends to celebrate his birthday. He drove my car out there and I noticed he wouldn't let me hold his phone for more than 20 seconds while reading navigation directions to him. "This is strangely suspicious, but I'll ignore it because I am such a cool girlfriend," I thought to myself.

The next day I was alone in the kitchen, having just frosted his second birthday cake after burning the first one I'd baked. I asked myself, "What would the World's Best Girlfriend do next? — Ooo I know! I'll make bean dip for everyone!" As I went to retrieve Ronald's Mom's Famous Bean Dip Recipe, I received an intuitive nudge.

Maybe I should check his text messages... while I'm here.

We regret to inform you this snooping session has confirmed your Boyfriend is cheating on you. Proceed as you wish.

NOOOOOOOOOOO OOOOOOOOOO OOOOOOOO

ABSS 3 G

The juicy details are for another book.

Paradigm Shift

What?! The man I LOVED & wanted to marry was CHEATING on me?! Lying to my face?? I felt deeply betrayed by Life & by MYSELF. HOW could I have been SO SURE of something that was not true?? (What ELSE might not be true?) To this day, I do not remember whether or not I actually made the Bean Dip, but I do remember feeling guided by a force greater than myself. I gathered my things, packed up my car, informed Ronald we were no longer in a relationship, and drove myself home.

Post-Traumatic Break Up Schedule

7pm: Have a surprisingly coherent & grown-up conversation with Ronald, ending with his saying "You want the moon? I'll give you the moon," trying to George Bailey me from <u>It's a Wonderful Life</u>.. but then denying the quote was from that Movie! (It is.) Further reinforcing my decision to LEAVE.

9pm: Purchase the Largest, stalest cup of Gas Station coffee imagineable.

9:07pm: Drive. Call everyone I Love & ask how Late I could call them Back, so as to fill every moment of my drive with eager, Loving, Listening Ears & Shoulders. I felt like I was George Bailey at the end of the movie [SPOILER ALERT!] when all of his dearest friends come to his rescue—I didn't even know I had that much Support in my Life ♡

I also experienced a Life-changing gas station coffee-related poop.

3:33AM: Arrive home to find my roommates had postered the walls with "Rosie the Riveter" images with my face Photoshopped in.

Happy Katie- EMPOWERMENT Day!

we can do it!

It was one of the most blissful and devastating days of my life. For the first time in a long time, I could FEEL my aliveness rushing through me. There were only two speeds: Feeling absolutely Nothing or absolutely Everything. It was similar to the experience I'd had when one of my best friends died unexpectedly Sophomore year of high school. The pain brought me to life in a new way, revealing the unexpected pleasure of being fully present with my experience. Is euphoria one of the stages of grief? It should be.

Upon arriving home in my new life, I was so present I didn't know what to do with myself. I woke up the next morning feeling like I needed to DO something with all my energy. My mind went to a pile of half-finished crafts in my closet. I furiously hot-glued my way to completing a wine cork corkboard and finally made myself a "God Jar" recommended by Julia Cameron in The Artist's Way.

I had worked through The Artist's Way creative Recovery Program (BOOK) months prior & discovered **LOADS** of my repressed CREATIVE DESIRES...

I want to Sing... but I'm Scared I'll be bad at it.

I want to MOVE to NYC and perform on SNL! ...but How?!

I want to make art & write & play all day, but that's not what grownups are supposed to DO!

Encountering this Strange Stillness & Upheaval in my Life made me realize...

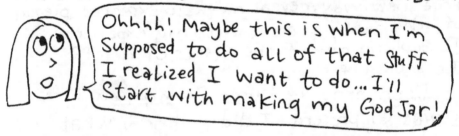

Ohhhh! Maybe this is when I'm supposed to do all of that Stuff I realized I want to do... I'll Start with making my God Jar!

"God Jar": (n.) a recepticle in which to place hopes, desires, thoughts & fears that are too big for me to hold alone. I made mine out of an empty Pomogranate Juice Glass.

(Here's the inaugural note I placed in my God Jar:

P♡M

Dear Artist,
This is a little letter to let you know
what simple changes you might want
to make in your life. You just broke
up with Ronald—GO YOU!—So you
should be able to find time to invest in
yourself a little more. Here are my ideas:

① Read something that inspires you.
   —you have a love/hate relationship with
   reading. Talk with friends about their
   favorite books & pick one that looks good!

② HANG OUT WITH YOUR FRIENDS
   [Insert List of Specific Friends I Miss]

③ RUN. Run, Katie, Run. It helps you
   so much to think clearly & feel
   powerful & more your body through
   this world without any help. Do it.

④ PAMPER YOURSELF. Get regular Manicures &
   Pedicures. Make your feet smooth. Use Lotion.

⑤ Organize & keep your room clean.

⑥ Stay Gluten Free—it makes you
   feel better.

⑦ Buy NEW ART SUPPLIES.

⑧ COOK MORE

⑨ Write Every Day. Morning Pages
   Night Pages. Lunch Pages.

⑩ Sign up for an Open Mic

⑪ Keep a Log of detailed observations.

LOOK CLOSELY.

Although I could see some of the ways my Life wanted to transform, putting my intellectual Knowing into action was easier said than done.

We might refer to this period of my Life as my "Dark Night of the SouL." I received many Wake up caLLs about ways I was Living out of aLignment, including, but not Limited to...

Finally, a flag red enough
to get my attention.

BULIMIA

Despite the many flags I had encountered along the way, I'd always been able to justify my food & body obsession with NORMALIZED aspects of Diet Culture.

I'm Losing weight in a SAFE way

FOOD is FUEL not Fun!

I'm healthy & FIT!

I cut out food groups for health reasons I've Googled.

I binged on Chex Muddy Buddies and then made myself throw up because I didn't want them in my body anymore because they're not healthy — OH WAIT. Making myself THROW UP isn't healthy either.

SYSTEM OVERRIDE: THIS IS NOT OKAY. THIS IS YOUR INNER WISDOM SPEAKING.

As every aspect of my identity was crumbling around me with the loss of the Love of my Life, I could not deny that the Truer Truth must live in this BLOB of spooky "Unknownness."

I could not deny the KNOWING that a deeper "me" wanted to be born, but my ego resisted entering the void every step of the way, sneakily tiptoeing back into my old self instead of surrendering to the truth of the present moment, afraid to feel the Bottomless pit of my grief. Even though I knew for certain I wanted to stop bingeing & purging, my bulimia persisted. At the time, I blamed it on hormonal birth control, my dumb doctor, my asshole boyfriend, but the truth is that Bulimia was my soul's way of getting my attention, saying "Come here, sweetheart. You can stop all the running. Let's get quiet. Just Listen." ♡

Bulimia: (n.) my body's refusal to digest life.

The person you wanted to marry cheated on you.

You've been pressing "snooze" on your creative dreams.

You just ate 5 gluten-containing chocolate chip cookies, 5 spoonfuls of peanut butter, & 10 finger-fuls of ice cream.

How about no?

Magical Monocle of Hindsight

Not only was I confronted with my deepest fears — the fear of abandonment, rejection, not belonging, not feeling worthy of love — I was also VISCERALLY experiencing MY OWN REJECTION of myself through the real-life metaphor of Bulimia.

One month after the BIG BREAKUP of 2014 and one week after my best friend married HER best friend (the two most opposite events my nervous system could have experienced), I was sitting alone on a flight to an improv festival in Canada.

Spending time with myself while traveling is when I feel the most "ME." Especially on planes. I am free to do whatever I want — no one is expecting anything or aware of what I'm doing (unless I tell them about it in a cartoon-based memoir I write years later (now!)).

On this particular flight, I was having a classic "FRANTICALLY FIGURE OUT MY LIFE!!!" session, which involves making a series of interlocking To-do lists, perhaps resembling a serial killer's attempt to plot "HOW TO LIVE A GOOD LIFE."

As I was coming up to take a breath from my perseverative ocean of doom, I heard a voice, felt a feeling, experienced a deep internal knowing with the message:

"I am always with you."

I didn't recognize the voice at first—
it was distinctly different from the
tirade of commands & internal bullying
I was accustomed to. "I am always with
you" —it was a message from the
"I" I really am, not the "I" I'd been parading
around as, who'd been silencing the real "I" for
years. She was coming forth to let me know
she hadn't given up on me. She would
never give up on me. This welcoming,
nurturing place is available to me any time,
no matter what I've done.

I cried on the plane in a sea of strangers,
touched by the remembrance of Unconditional
Love. I look back on this moment as the
first time I felt the presence of God—
Not the "God" I had learned about in Catholic
school, but the one I was writing notes to in my Jar, who had
always been with me, waiting for me to
accept the Ultimate Friend Request ♥

Okay, Let's get back on the

Eating — Disorder — Train

My momentary brush with the

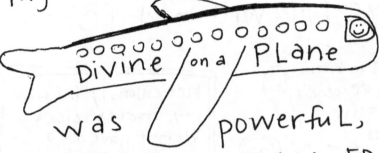

Divine /on a/ PLane

was / powerful,

but not quite enough to ERASE the illusion of Diet Culture I'd been under my whole life.

The mismatch between my inside & outside worlds was becoming increasingly apparent. My alarm was going off and I was lying awake in bed knowing I needed to get up, but not sure HOW to do that.

[Spoiler Alert: One slow, gentle step at a time ♡]

Struggling with food

Including counting calories, wanting my body to be smaller, weighing myself (at least) daily, bingeing, purging, restricting, compulsively exercising, etc.

was my (eventually ineffective, but effective at the time) way of avoiding Struggling with my Life.*

Wow! I'm working hard & expending creative energy!

Meticulously tracking my food & exercise & weight gave me a sense of Purpose, which I see now as having been a PLACE HOLDER for my higher Purpose of helping others wake up from the illusion of Meticulously tracking food & exercise & weight to derive PURPOSE.

*When I say "struggling with my life," I mean facing my life head on, being honest with the ways I'm living that do not feel in-alignment with who I really am. I mean having the humility to admit this to myself & then ASK for HELP.

(I hate asking for help...)

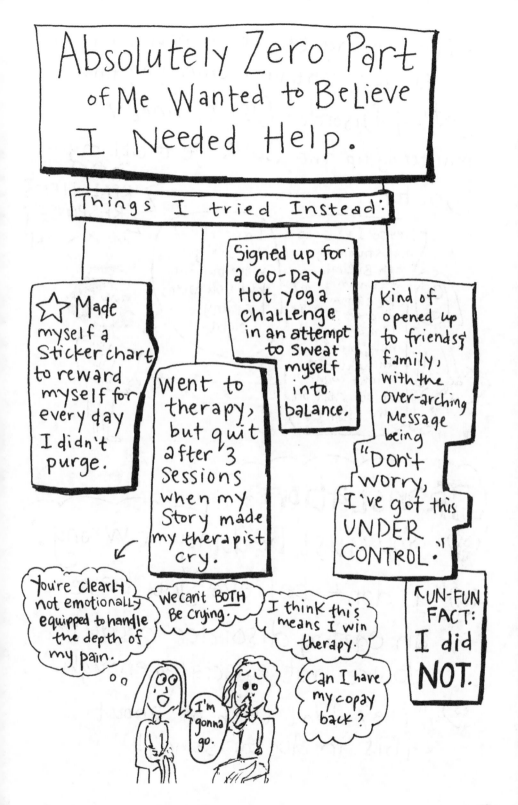

After firing (ghosting) my therapist, I slowly continued emerging from the Eating Disorder Closet, finally mustering up the COURAGE to tell my Doctor:

REAL-LIFE RESPONSE!

Hey, so I've kinda been struggling with Bulimia... you know... the eating disorder... I'm getting help, but I thought you might want to pop that on my chart.

I'm confused. You said you were bulimic, but you haven't lost any weight.

Translation:
💔 "You MUST be doing it wrong."
💔 "I don't believe you have an eating disorder because you're not emaciated enough."
💔 "They didn't teach me about this in doctor school!"

To Be Honest, I HAD NO IDEA How I would have wanted someone to respond to me when I told them about my brushes with Bulimia. That was part of the reason I kept quiet or down played my struggle — I didn't know what I needed. I was afraid people would be {Scared} or {Shocked} or that they'd try to FIX ME.

Nooooooo, NOT THAT!!

If I use my handy dandy Magical Monocle of Hindsight, I can see what words may have been helpful to hear...

Thank you for trusting me enough to share this with me.

I love and support you no matter what. Do you want to talk more about this?

From my Doctor:
What you're experiencing is not uncommon and is treatable. Here are some resources & referrals that could support your recovery.

Do you want any support in getting help?

You are not alone & this is not your fault. It is okay to take your time with recovery. This is a Life-Long Journey

And my doctor said, "But how could you have an eating disorder if you haven't lost any weight?" Like, "FYI, you're doing it WRONG!"

Is she naked behind that speech bubble?!

I gradually began to tell more people about my eating disorder, and even though I frequently downplayed how much I was struggling, Sharing my story was empowering & Shining a =Light= on my disease gave it Less Power over me. I signed up for a Stand Up Comedy class and discovered that Owning my Truth was the Ultimate Antidote to SHAME for me. Putting my particular perspective into a joke and hearing people laugh at it in resonance made me feel Less alone. My point of view wasn't "wrong," it was FUNNY! How do I feel about unsolicited pickles? Why is "makeout with a stranger at a bar" on my Bucket List? Why is Bulimia the most indecisive eating Disorder? Writing Stand Up was a way of getting intensely curious about my own unique experience, a feeling my soul was craving. My mind had been oblivious to this need, so preoccupied with trying to fix me, she didn't notice I simply wanted to be seen & heard.

Notes to My Past Self

Being honest with Others starts with Being Honest with MySelf♡

Honesty is Freedom.
The thing you are craving exists in telling your story.

Your truth is safe♡

Authentically admitting you do not feel Happy is the First Step to feeling AUTHENTIC HAPPINESS♡

Acknowledging you are doing, speaking or feeling out of alignment is the path to entering greater alignment♡

you're doing great & I Love you♡

Serendipitously as I was attempting to get more in touch with my inner truth, a good friend of mine asked if I wanted to take a Vision Boarding Class with her. "YES!" I thought. "This is how I will unlock my creativity & FIX My Life!"

It had truly never occurred to me that "inner peace" could be a goal. It sounded like a cop-out people used when they hadn't achieved their real goals.

"Inner peace is for sissies!" my subconscious programming retaliated against my vision boarding instructor's suggestion. "Don't you know who I am?! I'm a two-time valedictorian! I completed a 60-day Bikram yoga challenge in 59 days! I'm the former President of two major university student organizations I only half-wanted to be president of! I'm good at DOING stuff. What could 'just being' possibly have to offer me?!"

Right now, I want to

say to my former self, "Sweetheart, don't worry about choosing between being and doing. You get to have both as soon as you give up the fight of trying to "do" enough to prove you are worthy of this seat on the planet. Breathe. You are everything you think you need to be and more right now. Once you know that, really feel it in your bones, all the "doing" of life is extra. You could take it or leave it. You are doing more by allowing yourself to BE than you could ever DO otherwise."

But if I allow myself to just BE in this moment, I'll Let go of all the parts of myself I think I am!

Exactly! We call this an Ego-death; it feels like actual death except you get to KEEP LIVING, just without believing you're someone you're not. ♡

Helpful Buddhist

GLimpses
of
Mind/Body Connection

Throughout the stages of my disorder, I practiced

Yoga, but was mostly seeing it as a

way to shrink my body rather than connect
with it. My relationship with yoga has evolved
along with my recovery journey, but it alone
was not enough to transform my mind/body
connection like I'd been hopeful it would.

I experienced connection in fleeting
moments during yoga class, which would
usually make me cry — happy tears for the
experience of peace & bliss and sad tears for
the devastating realization this was not my normal
state.

One significant glimpse of
presence I experienced was my

first time **FLOATING** in a

Sensory Deprivation Tank...

An acquaintance from yoga class asked if I'd act in an instructional video he was filming for his friend's soon-to-be-opened Float Center.

I'm terrified of wearing a Bathing suit on camera, but I LOVE trying new things...

YES!!

He wanted me to get a feel for the experience — spending 60 minutes FLOating Weightlessly in epsom salt-rich Body-Temp water in a Pitch Black, soundproof Isolation Tank.

...sounds like more alone time than I've had in this whole Lifetime put together.

SPOILER ALERT: The video fell through so no bathing suit nightmare for me!

When I emerged from the tank, Lightness filled my Body & Mind. I felt like one of those people who are colorblind & then put on special glasses that let them See COLOR for the first time. In a post-FLOat voice memo I left for myself, I said,

Ohhhh. THIS is who I am. I forgot!!

"I feel like I got my Happiness Back!!" ♡

Before I could start Living at a FLoat Tank LeveL of JOY, I had to admit that what I'd been calling "happiness" was not ActuaL happiness.

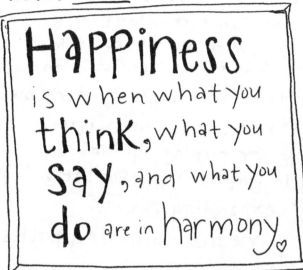

Happiness
is when what you **think**, what you **say**, and what you **do** are in harmony ♡

— Mahatma Gandhi

WeLL it's safe to say I'm NOT happy.

FinaLLy! That's the piece we've been waiting for!

THINK	"AM I happy?"
SAY	"I'm happy!"
DO	"I'm not happy." (AKA Torturing my Body)

THINK	"I'm not happy."
SAY	"I'm not happy."
DO	"I'm not happy."

So Because I'm harmoniously un Happy I'm somehow Happy?!

Soooo... How did you Recover?

Great question, me! It is impossible to pinpoint the exact moment my recovery began, or to attribute it to a singular method, book, or person. For me, Recovery has been a process of relearning how to trust my intuition as a guide for picking up tidbits, clues, and insights that RESONATE with me on a soul-expanding LEVEL.

Recovery means following paths that CHALLENGE what I believe rather than CONFIRM my existing beliefs in order to arrive at a TRUER TRUTH within me ♡

AKA shifting from my mind being in charge to my heart.

That being said, I would love to share the tid bits (and big bits) that have resonated with me on my recovery journey, trusting your intuition will know if they resonate with you too. ♡

Truth
Truth
INTUITION
Truth
Truth

Chapter 4
Choosing Recovery TREATS

1. **Surrender**

   3 Tbsp Butter & 1 pack marshmallows

   into a pan

   Over the heat of **Perceived Urgency**

2. When it's all melty, remove from heat & add 6 cups of **Willingness**

   A.K.A.

   whatever cereal you like

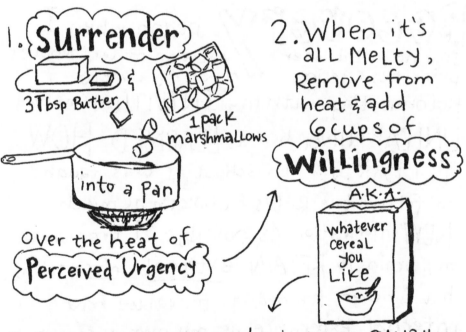

3. Spread mixture evenly into a 9×13" pan with **Unconditional Self-Love**

   Cool, cut, & enjoy!

I used to follow my OUT-tuition but now I follow my IN-tuition*!

* which costs ZERO tuition

Recovery began when I
saw how I'd been valuing other people's priorities & desires over my own♡

Reconnecting with my INTUITION involved UNLEARNING how I LEARNED HOW TO LEARN♡ In School, I was taught to follow the Rules & soak up as much NEW information as possible. I programmed my brain to RETAIN external information, but I never trained it to value my internal experience as my own personal connection to WISDOM♡

My recovery journey has been a gradual process of shifting my internal monologue from "Am I doing this right?" to "Does this feel Right to Me? Does this Light me up?"

I began dipping my feet into the infinity pool of my desires one little toe at a time.

Six months after my paradigm-shifting break up, I made the New Year's Resolution to leave my wonderful, yet comfort-zone-y Occupational Therapy job to pursue *acting* with my full time energy. I gave close to 8 months' Notice — mostly to give my terrified mind time to catch up with my courageous heart.

Around the same time, I started testing the waters of Tinder, the online dating app (in case by some Miracle these words are being read in a world where "Tinder" is not a household name).

After countless swipes, meandering small talk, and one conversation where I tried to convince a man not to cheat on his partner, I started talking to someone I *actually* wanted to meet in REAL LIFE.

Let's call him Gustavo
(because he likes that name).
· ♡ ·

From our text exchange, I knew
Gustavo was funny. The kind of funny
you can only be when you're a good
listener.

86

When we met in person over gin & tonics (which I had been budgeting for all day on my calorie counting app), Gustavo was quiet & shy —someone I would never be attracted to if I'd met him in Real Life.

I didn't know why he had shown up in my life. I thought perhaps I'd be the person to help him come out of his shell & heal his crippling social anxiety, but he ended up being the one to do that for me, quite unexpectedly.

On our second date, we went for a hike, which I usually hate, I told him, because I'm scared of going down hills and I always feel pressure to speed up.

"We can go as slow as you want," he said.

Wow! It's amazing that I don't hate hiking with you!

I could feel my body RELAX in Gustavo's presence, an unfamiliar experience for my nervous system.

After our slow & steady hike, we went out for dinner at a diner. He ordered a Reuben Sandwich, fries & Apple Pie and I ordered a safe & scared SOUP.

I could feel all of my FOOD FEARS bubble up, and instead of quietly suppressing them in an attempt to be a COOL GIRL like I would normally do, I decided to let Gustavo in on my Secret Thoughts:

I wish I could order a sandwich & fries, but I'm afraid I might make myself throw up if I eat that, so I got this soup I don't really want instead. I don't want to make myself throw up, but it's been happening lately & I'm working on figuring it out. I don't know why I'm telling you. Please don't be scared or feel like you need to help me!

I'm not scared.

Gustavo Listened & Cared without being overbearing & scared. He said helpful things without trying to FIX Me.

> Are you drinking enough water?

> Do you want a hug? Do you want a fry & a bite of my pie?

> You can tell me as much as you want. I like it, even though I might not know what to say back.

> *Eye Contact*
> *Active Listening*

Feeling comfortable sharing my inside thoughts with Gustavo eventually led me to discovering the ⸗PORTAL⸗ that exists in the moments of feeling triggered

> I really want to make myself throw up right now.

↑I said in tears after eating too much cereal one night.

> You know, it's normal to get too full sometimes. When that happens to me, I just WAIT. Eventually I feel better & get hungry again.

> ...what is this "waiting" you speak of? Surely I must DO something.

Waiting, huh? How do I do that?

Without judgment,

Aspire (breathe)

In & out and

Thank yourself for being present ♡

Gustavo didn't spell out this acronym for me, but he did sit with me & hold me as I struggled through learning how to be with my own discomfort. I hadn't had the courage to face myself in this way before.

Slowly, slowly I began to feel safer exposing the inner insanity I was subjecting myself to as I was consistently met with a loving, non-judgmental presence.

Bulimia humbled me. After years of thinking I had it all figured out, bulimia showed me I DID NOT. And for the first time, I was allowing myself to be seen in my humanity, my not-knowing-it-all utter confusion about being ALIVE.

I could feel energetically that all of me was welcome with Gustavo — my insecurities &

My Dreams.

A few months into Dating, I felt ready to brush off the cobwebs of my Artist's Way work & had the realization...

I think I need to move to NYC... Do you want to come?

Suddenly my intuition **YEAH!** to leave my job made even more sense ...'... I was meant to go on an adventure guided by my creative soul! I noticed my struggles with food became quieter when I began facing my fears & dreams head on. Knowing I could share anything *sticky* with Gustavo helped me SO MUCH. For example...

I had never lived with a partner before, so moving to NYC with Gustavo felt LOADED, especially because my parents had instilled the belief that I should never live with someone before getting married.

But when I shared my concerns with Gustavo, he responded in a way that made me feel like NO matter what happened — even if we were to break up — we would have each other's backs. We could be there for ourselves and take care of each other through anything if we simply focus on each day, each moment at a time.

Ahh yes, being PRESENT. This was one of the many gifts Gustavo brought me.

On the plane ride to New York, I read The Power of Now by Eckhart Tolle, which reinforced everything I was learning about LIVING in the PRESENT MOMENT. It made so much sense — Life is always happening

Right Now. Thinking constantly about the Past or Future was the source of my anxiety & struggle. While this concept didn't transform my brain overnight, it did COLOR the way I viewed my new Life in NYC. Even though Life did not become Suddenly *Perfect,* I began FLOWING WITH it instead of STRUGGLING AGAINST it.

On our First night in the city, my fears of being in a New place Surfaced & I tried to take them out on Gustavo — "This is all your fault!" But his calm, steady presence helped me catch myself in the moment.

As I began to see "imperfect" moments as PORTALS to PRESENCE, synchronicities emerged all over the place. The *Imperfections* of my life were actually Perfect (a concept that would solidify more later when I read The Gifts of Imperfection by Brené Brown).

For Example...

I had a
HANGRY
MELTDOWN
in the middle of Target whilst buying apartment supplies.

Perhaps I need to eat more than a protein bar for lunch.

I can TAKE BREAKS and ask for what I need.

Gustavo still loves me even when I'm a raving lunatic!

I didn't get a
CALL BACK
for a project
I REALLY wanted.

But I DID meet my first new friend at the audition, which felt like magic!!

I let myself feel SAD, while also feeling proud of myself for putting myself out there.

NYC was

Recovery to me ♥
I felt so alive & in
flow...

Performing in
& Producing
Standup
Shows

Co-Writing,
Producing &
Performing in
a Web series

Making New
FRIENDS

Acting
in acting
Class

Writing
Sketch
Comedy &
Starting a
team I
Liked

Somehow
eating & drinking
without bingeing &
Purging (I was
still restricting,
unbeknownst to me)

... Until one week about seven months
into Living in the city...

Gustavo's wonderful, generous Parents came to visit us...

As a chronic controller & restricter, nothing was more tempting & triggering than access to *whatever food I wanted.* Mind you, I had no idea of what I ever *actually* wanted to eat because I was always so rigid about eating the exact same things based on *healthiness* rather than tastiness. This week of many many meals eaten "out" followed by another week of "out" meals with other out-of-town guests ROCKED my RECOVERY WORLD — I had my first relapse of Bulimic Behaviors since I had moved to NYC.

Truth Secret: As I write this, I'm remembering I'd had other Bulimic experiences, mostly at Bottomless Mimosa Brunches I blocked from memory.

Disheartened and determined, I began Googling "Bulimia Outpatient Centers" to check myself into. In my opinion, they were all extremely expensive, which probably would have been my opinion no matter what they cost because I was not accustomed to investing ANY amount of money into my health and wellbeing.

♡

One day, I was writing standup with a friend and mentioned I was working on material about my eating disorder. She LIT UP—"Really? I'm in OA!" "What's OA?" "Overeaters anonymous." I LIT UP. "That sounds like exactly what I need!" On some level, what I heard was "FREE RECOVERY," which fired me up in the same way I might be fired up around a FREE SAMPLE table (my truest kryptonite). Either way, I could feel my reality was about to shift when I decided to go to my first meeting.

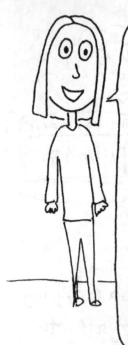

HeLLo! I'm here to tell on myself. I've been trying to run the show of my Life and pretend it's really fun & easy, but it's NOT! And when I try to fix it on my own, it never Lasts & I get caught in a spiral of trying to Control my way out of my control issues. Am I in the right place?

Twelve Step Recovery Shhhh!

Yes! Come on in!

As a Lifelong rulefollower, I debated about whether to explicitly include my experience in a 12-Step Recovery Program because it felt like I might be disgracing the tradition of anonymity, but I also realized it'd be impossible to FuLLy teLL my story of Recovery without including the 12-Steps. I'm not here to "promote" any particular program, but I also want to share how the steps changed my Life, demystify them in a way Like Russell Brand did in his amazing book, "Recovery" (I'm working off the Logic that "If Russell Brand did it, I can too!" Thanks for the Green Light, Russell.) My intention is to share what has worked for me because hearing what worked for others in the program Changed my Life… Perhaps sharing how the steps helped me go from feeling stuck to living in flow might help someone else get un-stuck as well. As with everything in this book (and in life), take what works and leave the rest!

I remember the *Last* time I binged and purged before joining OA. I drank too much at a party, just enough to let me eat half a tray of S'mores Rice Krispie Treats on the snack table. I felt so disgusting afterwards. When we walked into our Studio Apartment, I told Gustavo to "put some music on," our signal to each other we were going to poop and we'd like to protect the other from having to hear a poop plop. In the same way I would often have a "Last Supper" binge on all the carbs, chips & ice cream in my house before starting a new diet, I went to the bathroom and purged, knowing it would be the last time. I was ready to do whatever it would take to LET GO of this "Control-Z" behavior, which had been my on-again, off-again companion for the previous two years. Bulimia was my lover, Gustavo was my boyfriend. Or maybe it was the other way around. I emerged from the bathroom, turned off the symphony that was blasting and told Gustavo what had happened. I promised it was the Last time, though he would never ask me to promise that. I was promising Me.

Overeaters Anonymous was a series of truer & truer truth bombs - at first coming out of other people and eventually coming out of myself. There was nothing pretty or sugar coated about it. It was exhilarating being in rooms of individuals who were willing to cut through the bullshit of life and share themselves authentically. It didn't matter where anyone was on their journey; what we all had in common was a shared desire to witness and live our lives fully, hide nothing, discover the Reality behind our perceived reality. (Oh AND we all wanted to stop compulsively overeating.)

Where can I get my Gold Star for being a good Recovery person?

Of course, I immediately wanted to be "good" at it. It is hard for me to feel like a beginner at anything, but I had to admit I was a complete Newbie at this kind of Recovery. I was becoming aware of HOW MUCH I DID NOT KNOW, which put me in touch with what it meant to SURRENDER – letting go of "my way" of doing things and letting myself be seen fully – with all my imperfections.

For the first 6 months, I wasn't working with a sponsor, but I did get high on the recovery fumes at meetings. It was a relief to bring my full self to a space and share freely with a room full of non-judgmental, open listeners. Even as I'm writing now, I find myself editing my words in a way to make them more palatable to a larger audience (not intentionally, but I feel the subconscious filter present). For the first time, my Stream of Consciousness felt safe somewhere outside of a page. My story could be received without the painful grimaces I'd feared.

The game went from being "Try to make it look like everything is okay" to "stop trying to make it look like anything but what it is." ♡

Becoming a Shame Detective

Hiding & Keeping Secrets bottled up was one of the most debilitating parts of having an eating disorder. I held the false belief: "I should be able to fix this because it's coming from MY brain. Something must be wrong with me!"

OA helped me See that I had a DISEASE and I was not defined by it. I felt a weight lift off my shoulders when I let myself share what I'd been afraid to share before.

Healing Retreat ♡

Day 1: You are not Broken: you don't need fixing or healing.

I wish they would have mentioned that before we paid the registration fee.

My new Recovery Goggles helped me see that all of my tumultuous experiences with Food & My Body could be used as PORTALS into deeper truth.

My Relationship with food was showing me my relationship with Life. It wasn't comfortable to look at, but once I saw it, I couldn't un-see it. I continued forward in the direction of truth.

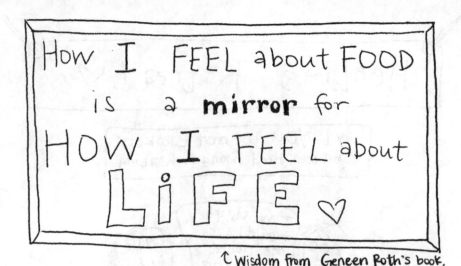

How I FEEL about FOOD is a mirror for HOW I FEEL about LiFE ♡

↳ Wisdom from Geneen Roth's book, _Women, Food, and God_

What I've Done with Food

Binge-eating trail mix hurriedly over the sink as soon as I'm home alone.

Meticulously calculate & document calorie intake & exercise

weigh myself to determine how I feel

Binge & purge

REFLECTION →

Hidden Beliefs About Life

- I'm afraid of not having enough, fear of scarcity.
- I've been hiding who I am & what I want.
- I can only be myself when I'm alone.

- "I Need to be in control."
- I'm afraid of the unknown.
- The world will reject me if I'm not a certain size

I'm afraid I'm not good enough. I need external validation to feel okay.

Life is too much for me to process or digest. I feel like I want more of something, but I don't know what.

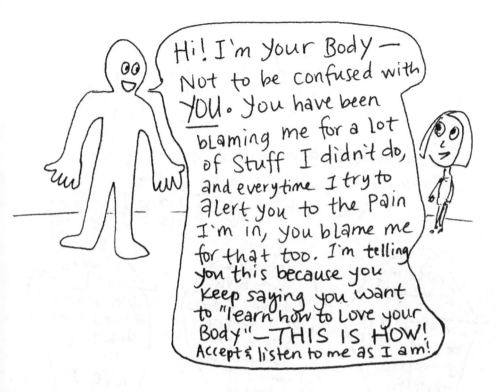

For my entire life, I had been mistaking my body for myself. Every piece of discomfort I felt internally, I saw mirrored externally in a "problem area." My body was the scapegoat I used to avoid facing the true struggle underneath.

> Important Reminder: My idea that a body should look a certain way was largely inherited from Systemic Fatphobia, from living in a world where body-blaming is NORMALIZED.

Just the Tip

of inherited, generational, ancestral trauma disguised as body hatred A.K.A. the Iceberg

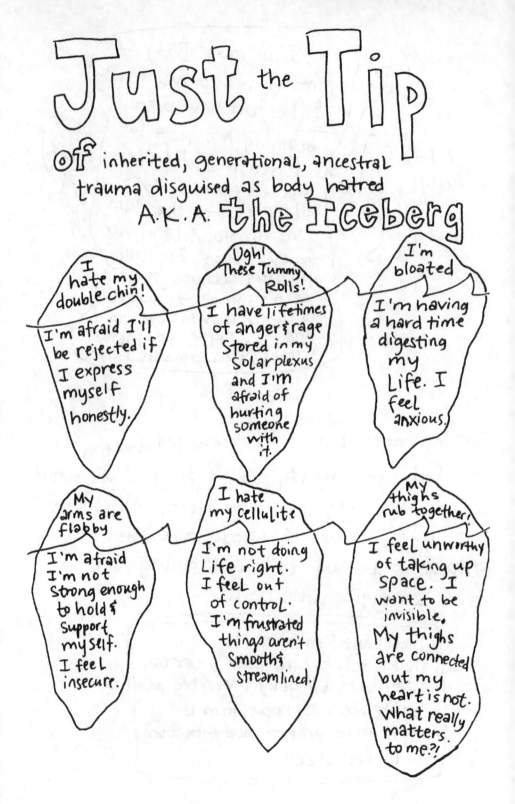

I hate my double chin!

I'm afraid I'll be rejected if I express myself honestly.

Ugh! These Tummy Rolls!

I have lifetimes of anger & rage stored in my solar plexus and I'm afraid of hurting someone with it.

I'm bloated

I'm having a hard time digesting my Life. I feel anxious.

My arms are flabby

I'm afraid I'm not strong enough to hold & support myself. I feel insecure.

I hate my cellulite

I'm not doing Life right. I feel out of control. I'm frustrated things aren't smooth & streamlined.

My thighs rub together!

I feel unworthy of taking up space. I want to be invisible. My thighs are connected but my heart is not. What really matters to me?!

The Feelings Wheel

In Recovery, my "I feel fat" alarm became helpful for Noticing where & when I was feeling discomfort. I set an intention to be gentle with myself in these moments and respond with Curiosity instead of judgment.

Recovery is NOT a Final Destination, it's a DAILY Choice.

The OA program helped me see what "Choosing Recovery" meant for me.

Looking back, I can see my own Personal equation looks something like this:

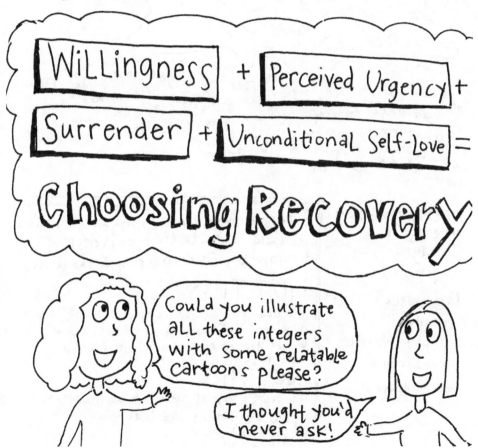

Willingness often arises

when we wake up in a pile of our own shit. ♡

I'll do anything to get out of here.

...nay, a Mountain Range of our own shit.

The size of it does not matter — you get to decide if it is enough to inspire your willingness to change. And there is no shame in not-changing. Sitting in the pile — even being willing to admit it *might* be there is a tremendous act of courage. ♡

As Elizabeth Gilbert once said on Instagram, and Emily McDowell & friends @emilymcdowell — Turned into a Greeting Card.

Everyone who ever changed their life or Laid Claim to their own destiny began by surrendering to two words:

NOT THIS.

It's okay if you don't know yet what happens next. You just have to be honest about what your deepest truth is telling you. which is:

NOT THIS.

If that's what your body, heart, and soul are trying to tell you:

LISTEN.

Perceived Urgency

← Because I can choose how "urgent" any change is that I want to make ♡

Hmm... I should probably address this obsession I have with diet & weight & exercise... maybe next month!

JK I would NEVER have → weighed myself with clothes on

VS.

I don't know what my "boundaries" are, but I definitely know I just crossed one.

Something needs to change now!

YEARS of NON-URGENT Dieting HELL
manifesting as a dull roar of an internal dialogue I mistook for myself

The Moment I made Myself Throw Up for the first time, Change Felt Urgent.

While my bingeing & purging continued off and on for two more years and a felt sense of recovery came in spurts & took even longer to settle inside of me, a huge shift happened the moment my gut & my brain decided SIMULTANEOUSLY "this is not okay." Instead of passively going along for the ride my subconscious patterning wanted to take me on, I felt an urgent pull to actively change my trajectory.

Surrender

letting go of the addictive
ILLUSION of CONTROL
to allow for the
Reality of the messy, uncertain,
ever-changing,
magnificently simple

PRESENT Moment

to guide me
HOME to
myself ♡

Mantra of Surrender:
"This is exactly
what is supposed
to be happening
right now. Especially
the ugly parts—
these are helping my
transformation the most." ♡

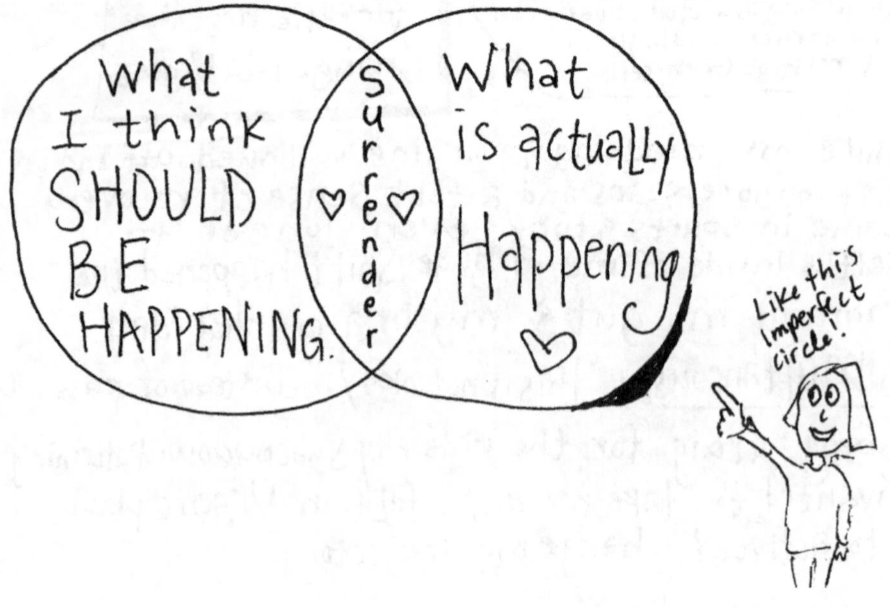

What
I think
SHOULD
BE
HAPPENING.

Surrender
♡   ♡

What
is actually

Happening
♡

Like this
imperfect
circle!

Unconditional Self-Love

(A popular & effective off-shoot of the
Classic "Unconditional Love")

A Practical Step-by-Step Guide
♡ to Loving the Heck out of Yourself ♡

1. Become a non-judgmental observer of your thoughts and actions.

2. Love every little bit of every thought & action that comes up.

3. Repeat to infinity.

In a way that still Feels Authentic

Fun Fact: Loving the parts of myself I'd prefer to pretend aren't there IMMEDIATELY increases my capacity to have compassion for others— especially the ones I judge the most ♡

Wow. I really hate how my body looks today.

I hate that I hate how my body looks. I hate that my looks matter to me.

I Love the part of myself that is judging myself, and the part of myself judging me for judging myself.

I Love this body who never asked to be verbally or mentally abused like this! She's done nothing wrong.

I love the part of you that thinks how you look matters.

I love how delightfully complicated my brain can be.

I Love the part of you that still doesn't believe me.

113

Chapter 5

Honesty Happy Hour

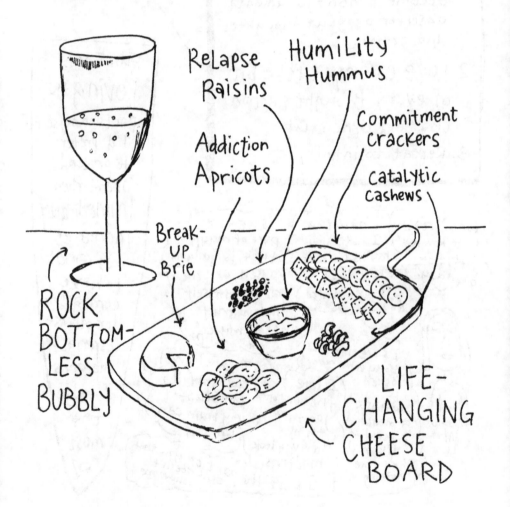

Relapse Raisins

Humility Hummus

Commitment Crackers

Catalytic Cashews

Addiction Apricots

Break-Up Brie

ROCK BOTTOM-LESS BUBBLY

LIFE-CHANGING CHEESE BOARD

By my calculations, I'm 3 mojitos, 2 protein shakes, and 5 pounds away from ETERNAL JOY.

Soon after joining OA, I realized my relationship with food mirrored my relationship with ALCOHOL. Growing up, I viewed drinking in a similar way to how I viewed dieting: There was a hidden power behind it that I wasn't allowed to access... YET. I didn't drink at all in High School — an easy decision for me based on obedience, fear of the unknown, and never being asked. In college, I was ready to be asked and responded immediately, "Why yes I would like a ladle of your mysterious Jungle Juice elixir," embarking on my quest to unearth the ever-elusive grown-up secrets behind drinking. Much like dieting, drinking brought with it many highs, but they often left me wanting more♡

Alcohol was my **Truth juice.**
It dissolved the meticulously constructed
barriers around my heart and gave me
permission to Feel my Feelings. Hard
and Fast. I was sure to weep at any
wedding with an open bar — first because
of how beautiful it was and later upon
realizing I, too, wanted to share my
unconditional love with another person
Forever & ever. Many wedding after-after parties
went like this:

Me: I think I want to Marry you!!
Ronald: You're too drunk to talk about this.
Me: No, I'm finally drunk <u>enough</u> to be honest about
   how I feel. I love you and I want to marry you!
Ronald: <u>I</u> can't talk to you when you're like this.
Me (to me): Hmm... It really sounds like he doesn't
   want to marry me, but I'm going to keep believing
   that deep down he DOES! How long will this take? Three
   more years of being a "chill" girlfriend? DONE!

Though I wasn't aware of it at the time, **ALCOHOL** was a **Gateway** to feeling my feelings ♡

...which was **HELPFUL** because...

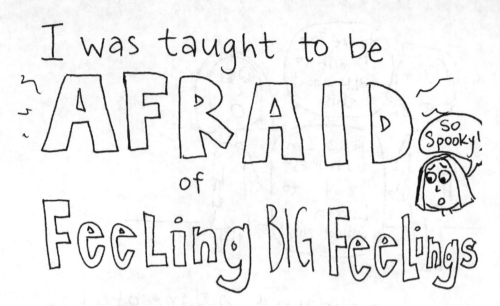

I was taught to be AFRAID of Feeling BIG Feelings

So spooky!

If "Feeling Class" were part of the core curriculum in schools, I'm convinced bullying & addictions would become unnatural. When we have no healthy way to process feelings, it makes sense that we develop coping mechanisms like addictions & eating disorders to make ourselves feel safe.

I feel out of control in my life, so I will rigidly control my food intake.

I'm afraid of being rejected, so I'll ignore my own needs in favor of pleasing others.

I believe I'm only worthy of existing if I'm being productive, so I'll work myself into a burnout.

addiction: (n) any behavior or substance consumed to create a temporary (and false) sense of Well-Being.

Addiction

← The wounds & accompanying Feelings I've been afraid to feel.

There's nothing wrong with using bandaids, but that wound is starting to get oozy and gross. I think it needs some air.

I'm using the word "Addiction" to normalize it — I'm referring to it as an experience of "doing or using something to make myself feel better." It's almost always an attempt to "feel _better_" rather than FEEL.

Recognizing the usefulness of my addictive patterns has helped me release the SHAME around them. My coping mechanisms have all been attempts to help me feel Safe, Loved, & more Like myself. But at a certain point, my "self-Love" shortcuts Stopped working and it became more useful to begin peeling away the Bandaid to feel what was festering underneath.

Awareness
transforms
Addiction

I began to see addictive patterns as a game
I play to avoid whatever feels
complicated about life. Just as my
periods of rigid "dieting" & rule-following
often see-sawed with periods of out-of-control
Bingeing & chaos, obsessing over self-improvement
often see-sawed with self-sabotage. Both
sides of the see-saw are addictions until
I choose to step off & stop playing the game.

The summer I joined OA, I started and ⸛finished⸛ writing a pilot script for the first time in my life by listening to and following the voice of inspiration, in the same way I'm writing this book— showing up every day to allow words to move through me. It felt like a creative renaissance. Standup was chugging along. I became more okay, more awake, more aware of my desires & more aware I was connected to a Source of unconditional love & support (aka a Higher Power aka God, the one from the jar, the one from the plane, the one I had access to all the time who spoke to me like a loving best friend). As my awareness grew, so did the uncomfortable knowing that it was time to end my relationship with Gustavo. I could feel myself teetering on the edge of resenting him when I'd talk about wanting to build a future together and he'd respond with the same "I don't know what I want" he'd been saying for two years. The beauty of our relationship is that I never expected or wanted him to be any different than he was, and he never expected or wanted me to be any different than I was. This worked well until my dormant desires to have a family & a partner & a big beautiful creative life were awakened within me.

As I became more in touch with my Higher Power, I began to see how Gustavo had been my surrogate Higher Power, an angel brought into my Life to remind me of who I was, to speak to me in the gentlest, sweetest voice, to listen to me with the gentlest, sweetest ears, to laugh at all my (good) jokes, to play with, to cuddle with, to Love on, to be loved by.

Gustavo was the Closest I'd come to Meeting God ♡
[and the closest I'd come to having a puppy]

Two weeks after I lovingly ended my
two year relationship with Gustavo, I
lovingly ended my 10 year relationship with alcohol.

What do I Really Want?

A Blog Post from October 2017 ♡

I quit drinking on December 16, 2016, the day before my 28th Birthday. My last drink might have been a couple of nights before that when my dinner was free samples (of wine, crêpes, milkshakes, alcoholic milkshakes, meatball sliders, cookies, sushi, apple cider, and everything else imaginable) before performing on my Birthday Week Stand up show, which devolved into some sort of open bar situation where I kept drinking because it was free, duh! (It turns out "free-ness" is my main reason for doing most things. You __can__ put a price on my dignity, and it's $0.)

On the 2AM Subway ride home, I had to transfer trains and my train was 10 minutes away so I ran out of the Subway Station for this brief window to go to Duane Reade and buy the cheapest BOX of cookies they had. Not even my favorite cookies— I didn't say, "Hey it's my birthday, I'm going to get myself something I like for a treat!" It was more like, "Hey, body? I hate you, and you've already eaten too many things today, so I'm going to continue filling you with as much crap as possible, and NO you don't deserve the good crap—you're going to eat this $2 Box of off-brand vanilla rectangle wafer cookies that taste like packing peanuts stuck together with a modest amount of sugary cream filling. HAPPY BIRTHDAY BODY!"

I hated what I was doing in the moment, but I had no way of stopping myself. Honestly, the gross cookies were a better choice than drunkenly making out with a friend at the bar, which would have produced a similar effect.

Upon my annual existentially-charged birthday reflections, I finally got honest enough with myself to admit that drinking was not contributing positively to my life. Having disordered thoughts about food was already like being in a controlling, abusive relationship with myself, and alcohol brought that out even more—"Ooo! Katie let her guard down. Let's eat all the donuts and pizza and packing peanut-esque wafer cookies she never lets us have!"

In the clarity of sobriety, I've come to realize my problems with alcohol and food weren't really about alcohol and food at all—a concept I'd heard and intellectually understood, but didn't fully understand until I'd experienced it. Sobriety gave me the boundary I needed to be able to pause & ask, "What do I really want?" What am I looking for when I pour myself a third (or 10th) glass of wine? Or gaze longingly into the glowing abyss of the refrigerator when I'm not hungry? Or stick my finger into a jar of my roommate's peanut butter? Or buy mediocre cookies at 2AM? Or log into Facebook when I just checked it 20 million times 5 minutes ago? What am I hoping to find? (Usually for me, it's connection, comfort, love, acceptance, validation, feeling fearless & uninhibited. All of that fun stuff.)

What do I really want? (continued again)

Obsessing over food & my body was a way to make food the thing that was challenging for me instead of confronting what was challenging about life. It really IS an effective avoidance strategy — it gives you a whole new category of things to worry about! Instead of facing my fears around putting my creative work (this!) into the world for instance, I could deal with the problem of having eaten half a jar of peanut butter, which I'd often deal with by eating more peanut butter and then going to hot yoga to off-set it and not eating for the rest of the day unless I got really hungry later and could maybe have a protein shake if I log all my calories on my Diet app and the math checks out. And then I could go to bed feeling *productive* for micromanaging my food and exercise, not realizing MY BODY HAS THAT COVERED. I can spend my energy on other things...like feeling my feelings, expressing myself, sharing my sweet little soul with the world.

In a way, I'm grateful for being a compulsive eater and drinker because it's brought more honesty into my life. Today, living in Recovery isn't about perfectly executing some sort of meal plan or following a rigid set of rules; it's more about noticing when I'm using substances as a substitute for real life; it's about showing up authentically even when it's uncomfortable; it's about pausing in the middle of my 5th trip to the refrigerator to ask myself, "What do I REALLY want?" The answer often changes, but I know I've never found it at the bottom of a jar of peanut butter or bottle of wine ♡

I officially quit drinking on my Birthday Eve, which happened to be the day before our multifaceted party.

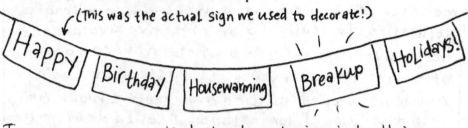

(This was the actual sign we used to decorate!)

Happy | Birthday | Housewarming | Breakup | Holidays!

I was nervous-excited about venturing into this event with my newfound resolute sobriety — what if I have no fun? What if I cave and have a drink? What if this confirms my fear that I can't do hard things? To my absolute surprise and delight,

Being Sober felt like a Super PoweR.

I could remember every detail of the night with such crispness. Living at the edge of this slightly uncomfortable new behavior of not-drinking at a party was like living at the surface of my life. I could feel more joy, perceive more nuances of social behavior, know when it was time to go to bed. It was like waking up from a fog.

OH! Parties don't have to mean I eat tortilla chips and drink gin & sodas until I want to die — there are PEOPLE here, with eyeballs I can look into and souls I can connect with. What a Magical World we live in!

My Sobriety high ensued for days—weeks even—but it was challenging going into environments where I was accustomed to connecting with friends & family with alcohol. Here is a verbatim text exchange with Gustavo from Christmas Day:

Me: Merry Christmas! I miss you! I am really wanting to drink some wine but also trying to remember that I don't REALLY want to because wine won't make me happy and it'll just muddle up my experience of the present moment.

G: Yeah you don't want that shit!

Me: Yeah then I'm just drunk cousin Katie instead of fun cousin Katie! I'm very fun!

G: Yeah don't let them give wine all the credit for how fun you are!

Me: YES thank you! The goal is to make people wonder "How much wine has Katie had?!" And then when they find out it's none they'll think "Wow, Katie is super fun!!"

G: Exactly. How will they find out it's none though? You'll have to perform some feat of coordination.

Me: That's tricky because I'm not very coordinated to begin with. A handstand perhaps?

G: That's perfect! They'll think, "Wow Katie must be hammered, she's doing a handstand in a dress I—what?? Perfect form??? Katie's FUN!!!

I adopted brand new Life Mottos...

I'm sick of alcohol getting credit for how much fun I am!

The Sober Drunk Text

I can still send potentially regrettable & vulnerable texts at ungodly hours of the night.

I'm living my best drunk life as a SOBER PERSON ♥

I'm done altering my state of consciousness to make you seem more fun ♥

For me, it is helpful to view my relationship with alcohol, food, dieting, exercise, my body by asking "What has this relationship taught me— what has it unlocked within me?" (This is also how I like to view actual relationships with people, too.) How can I honor the good this substance or behavior brought me?

ALCOHOL

Showed me how fun & carefree I am. She taught me that the thing on the tip of my tongue is usually either true or funny— sometimes both! That my fears are silly most of the time. That I am silly most of the time. That I am a great dancer. I'm very competitive. I'm good at flirting and making friends ♥ I love everyone. No, I really do. I love every single person on this planet. I will tell you about it until I cry— watch me. I am grateful for alcohol. I am also grateful for

Dieting.

Dieting taught me I have incredible determination and strength. When I am focused on a goal, I will accomplish it. I do have agency. When something does not feel right, I can take steps to change it. An external measure of success is never as satisfying as internal measures of success.

Bulimia

gave me the gift of finally admitting
something was *WRONG,* a reality
I may have continued to deny if I kept
"getting by" with my food & body obsession
that was so normalized by the world around
me. Bulimia put me in touch with my
desire to be emptied, to pour myself out,
like I'm doing now with my words. At the
time, I was too afraid of what truth would
emerge if I really allowed myself to be seen.
Bulimia showed me that This is what I was
missing from life — taking in experiences, digesting
them, allowing myself to be moved by my
life, allowing myself to be still. It put me
in touch with the unbearable-ness of being
a human and put me in touch with the
resilient part of myself that could feel
this depth of pain and still say, "I want
to live. I wish to continue. Sign me up
for one more day." It introduced me to
the scared child inside of me who
desperately needed to be helped and held
and began the awakening process of the
nurturing, loving parent inside of me who
could hold her in infinite unconditional
love, saying "I've got this, babe."

...which brings me to **GOD** (a word that still feels loaded after 13 years of Catholic School... Higher Power, The Universe, LOVE, Nature, Oneness, Great Creator, [Insert Your name for God here] all work too!).

I'd feel like an imposter talking about my Recovery without making the entire thing about Surrendering to a Higher Power. If OA showed me anything, it was THIS core Truth — I'm NOT DOING Life, I'm allowing God to do Life Through me.

CONGRATULATIONS!
You've made it this far to discover the Secret behind Door #3:

I'm not special, I just open myself up as a channel of God's infinite Love & Power That Everyone has access to!

To mix metaphors, I have no intention of pretending to be the ALL Powerful Wizard of Recovery (Oz). I'm inviting you behind the curtain.

In fact, before recovery, my Life FELT like I was that maniacal little man fiddling with his gears & gadgets desperately trying to control the show like the Wonderful Wizard of Oz.

I don't drink, but I do cry & trip a bunch!

FUN → Less Fun →

At the same time I decided to stop drinking alcohol, I also decided to stop eating sugar, which proved to be a bit too much "stopping" all at once. On Christmas, I caved, giving myself permission to eat sugar, even though I could hear a voice in my head saying "You shouldn't be eating that second cream puff!" (This was before I learned about intuitive eating.) Eating a moderate dessert turned into "helping with cleaning up" AKA finishing all abandoned goodies & sweets like a garbage disposal Christmas Elf. I had the icky feeling of having crossed my own boundaries, which continued happening over the following days, until one day when I was home alone & I ate every single frozen Christmas cookie, finished the pumpkin pie in the fridge, and had a smattering of other less memorable food items and then made myself throw up for the first time since I had entered Overeaters Anonymous 7 months prior. It was an unmistakable, undeniable, devastating RELAPSE.

Hello! I'm here to eat all the cookies Santa doesn't want!

A note about the name
"Overeaters" anonymous:

I did identify as a compulsive overeater, but it stemmed from compulsive restricting & controlling — whether it was emotional restriction (thinking "I shouldn't be eating this cream puff" while eating it) or physical restriction (like when I limit my carb or fat intake and my body does what it's evolutionarily DESigned to do & binges as a way of foraging for the key nutrients it's missing). Either way, what I used to consider "overeating" was really a natural response to deprivation & trying to control my food intake in one way or another. "Abstinence" (what OA calls "sobriety") for me is really an abstinence from the food obsession, from restriction, from bingeing & purging. It is less about eating a certain way and more about reconnecting to balance & sanity. It's not always black and white — though at the same time, "NO bingeing & purging" was my clear-cut bottom line abstinence. It was CLEAR I had broken it.

...AND IT SCARED ME. I reached out to the fellowship I didn't even know, ones I had met on a phone meeting while being home for the holidays. I spoke to women who comforted me, but didn't baby me; who saw me in my pain and said "If you want to hear what worked for me, I can share my experience."

Mountain of curiosity and openness

Cave of Isolation

The kindness, openness, and gut-wrenching honesty of the women I reached out to for support helped me stay open-hearted and curious instead of shutting down and retreating even further into my cave of secretive eating disorder heLL.

There was nothing to hide from these Loving strangers.

"I surrender the fight I've been having with an invisibLe opponent. I'm done trying to be right. I'm sick of doing things 'my way.' I'm willing to humbLe myself enough to ask 'what worked for you?'" That was the week I met Jodi, one of the women from the phone meeting.

MEMO
To whom it may concern:
I am officially DONE pretending to be fine.

J: "I can only share what worked for me — putting down my binge foods and finding a sponsor to take me through the steps." I loved her clear, direct, no-nonsense, almost abrasive tone.

Me: "Will you take me through the steps?" A slight pause and then —

"Yes, definitely. Your willingness is high right now

J: because you just relapsed. I can't and will never push or force you to recover, but if you are willing to do the work, I am willing to guide you."

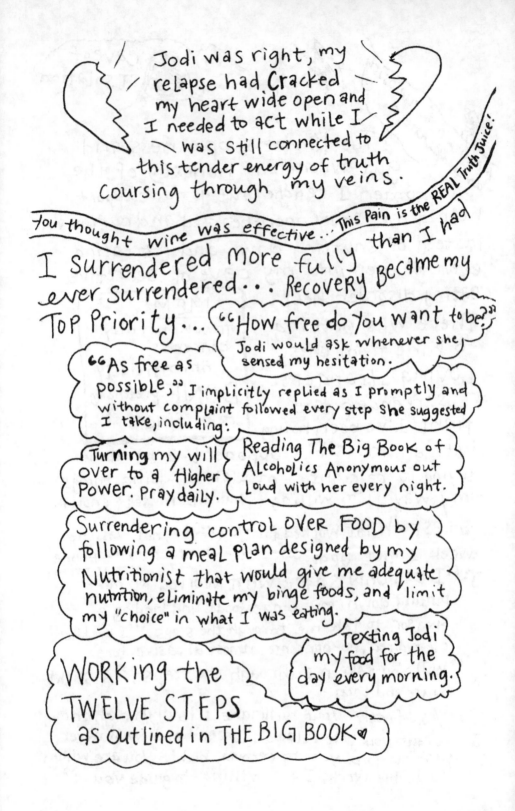

Jodi was right, my relapse had cracked my heart wide open and I needed to act while I was still connected to this tender energy of truth coursing through my veins.

You thought wine was effective... This pain is the REAL Truth Juice!

I surrendered more fully than I had ever surrendered... Recovery became my Top Priority...

"How free do you want to be?" Jodi would ask whenever she sensed my hesitation.

"As free as possible," I implicitly replied as I promptly and without complaint followed every step she suggested I take, including:

Turning my will over to a Higher Power. Pray daily.

Reading The Big Book of Alcoholics Anonymous out loud with her every night.

Surrendering control OVER FOOD by following a meal plan designed by my Nutritionist that would give me adequate nutrition, eliminate my binge foods, and limit my "choice" in what I was eating.

Texting Jodi my food for the day every morning.

WORKING the TWELVE STEPS as outlined in THE BIG BOOK♡

Chapter 6
12 (step) Layer Dip

Dipping into the
Twelve Steps ♡

This is the
CLASSIC RECIPE
with my own
twist! Great
for parties,
dining home
alone, befriending
new neighbors, etc.

The Twelve Steps

~Adapted by ME~
Based on "The Big Book of Alcoholics Anonymous"

It's not about *arriving* at the top of your mountain, it's about finding a way to trek it instead of avoid it.

The Steps are designed to facilitate a paradigm shift— The ability to see Life from a Newer, Truer Vantage point.

And it's gorgeous every step of the way!

Wow! I'm not the only one who's faced a seemingly insurmountable mountain!

Service
Awareness
Perseverance
Discipline
Love
Humility
Willingness
Integrity
Courage
Faith
Hope
Honesty

I Humbly admit I misspelled "humility"

The way things have always been

Oh boy...

There are many ways to traverse the mountains of Life — The Steps are Just one of those ways. For me, the Steps were a big factor in my Recovery & continual transformation, so I will do my best to Share my experience with them in a way that feels both true to me & digestible. I am NOT here to force the STEPS down anyone's throat ♡ As with everything in this book (& in Life), TAKE WHAT WORKS AND LEAVE THE REST.

whatever feels like ROCK BOTTOM

Fun Fact: We can decide ANY moment is our Rock bottom, our Last Straw & choose to transform our Lives ♡

#1
Anonymous Times
Best Seller
—
over 2 million
Lives changed

the life-changing
magic of tidying up
your side of the street
the art of taking an honest and
loving look at your life

I like to describe the Twelve Steps as a version of
Marie Kondo's book "The Life-Changing Magic of Tidying Up,"
except instead of tidying up your literal home,
you tidy up your internal home (perhaps an even
more literal home). I had gotten used to my
home as it was — my junk drawers overflowing, my
closet bursting at the seams, vegetables rotting at the
bottom of my fridge, a smattering of dirty Tupperware
containers collecting in the backseat of my car — I wasn't
aware every aspect of my life could use an overhaul.

I am now grateful for the relapse of bingeing & purging I had over the holidays – it was the uncomfortable wake up call I needed to get in touch with my own powerlessness. After months of believing I had this behavior "under control", I was confronted with a deeper level of surrender available to me. Instead of feeling safe & in control because I had "power over" my disease, I discovered more authentic power and safety that came from admitting I was not in control.

A quick note about POWER...

Step 1 is admitting I'm "powerless"?! Isn't that a little... disempowering?

It might sound that way, but the first step to becoming authentically empowered is to disempower all the ineffective methods we're using to feel powerful.

It is shifting from a "power over ____" perspective to one of "authentic power"

Power OVER:
"I have everything UNDER CONTROL."

Authentic POWER:
"I am confident, trusting, and whole. I admit I don't have control over everything, but I am open to seeing life clearly & honestly and following the guidance of a Higher power."

By admitting I am powerless "over" food, I make space for a Higher Power to enter my life...

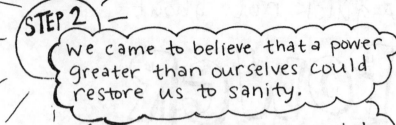

STEP 2

We came to believe that a power greater than ourselves could restore us to sanity.

AKA "I could use some help cleaning up this mess."

Are you there Marie Kondo? It's me, Katie.

For me, step 2 meant facing the fact that my way of doing life was no longer working for me. Although I had a lifetime's worth of preconceptions about [the "G" word] rooted in my Catholic conditioning & various inherited view points, it was clear to me that I was NOT the most powerful being in the universe; there must be a POWER greater than myself.

I was inspired to learn I could "create" my own Higher Power & that my Higher Power would inevitably be co-creating that image with me. (No blasphemy going on over here, Dad ☺) For me, Discovering how much fun it is to be in connection with God was the real selling point. It felt like making a new friend (best friend). One of my favorite poems that captures this feeling is "The Seed Cracked Open," by the 14th Century Sufi Poet, Hafiz.

The Seed Cracked Open

It used to be
That when I would wake in the morning
I could with confidence say,
"What am 'I' going to
Do?"

That was before the seed
Cracked open.

Now Hafiz is certain:

There are two of us housed
In this body.

Doing the shopping together in the market and
Tickling each other
While fixing the evening's food.

Now when I awake
All the internal instruments play
The same music:

"God, what love-mischief can 'We' do
for the world
Today?"

—Hafiz

Here is a Stream of Consciousness Journal Entry I wrote days after Taking Step 3...

RECOVERY Time Capsule

♡ January 4, 2017 ♡

I want to wake up every morning and talk to God. Guess what— you can! My spiritual-ity goes hand in hand with my creativity. God wants me to live in love —not bound by fear. God loves me no matter what I do. My Higher Power wants me to create from a place of openness and curiosity. My Higher Power wants me to treat others with love & approach the unknown with openness & curiosity instead of fear. God, grant me the serenity to accept the things I cannot change, the courage to change the things I can, and the wisdom to know the difference. It's the wisdom part I have trouble with. I secretly believe I'm in charge of the whole universe —I know how everything works & even if I don't know, I could figure it out. (And if I don't know, how important could it be anyways?) I, I, I. Me, me, me, STOP. Bring your eyes up from the page of your own story and realize there are millions of stories all around you —many of them more robust, interesting, funny, engaging, edifying than yours. I'm not telling you to feel shitty about your shitty story, but to approach everything and everyone as a student with openness and curiosity. Ask. Listen. Stop talking. Stop worrying about the next thing you have to say. Just BE, Respond, Love. Accept the love that comes to you. Thank you for this new day and all the new days. If I approach life as a gift, every moment becomes more enjoyable ♥

I had simultaneously started The Artist's Way again... ♡

♡ January 5, 2017 ♡

This stuff* takes work. (*Everything good & worthwhile in life.) I need to remember every day that I choose God's will over my will. I surrender anew each moment. I hear my own will whisper, "Yoga now! Go to yoga!" And I know in my gut that is not God's plan.

God is my Peaceful Intuition.

What is my peaceful intuition telling me?

Pause. Write your pages. Today is Saturday, take it slow & easy. Take the relief you are getting from program and use it to direct your energy to whatever you feel called to do. Write some standup in peace, Katie. Organize & dance around your apartment in peace, Katie. This is the beginning of your big beautiful life. Let me in. Let me show you, remind you what you love, what makes you feel full now that your obsessive, compulsive eating is quiet. Let me show you how to feed your artist, your sweet malnourished artist. You've created a war torn, tumultuous environment for her to live in. Surrender humbly to the creator and feel the fun of creating. There is magic. There is inspiration. You do not need to bring a #2 pencil & paper, just open your eyes. Watch and listen. Say Thank you.

Yes, Gustavo was your Higher Power & that was such a gift to be shown How you want to be loved. I want to be loved gently, unconditionally, without judgment, with humor & companionship. My Higher Power is fun. My Higher Power inspires me. I need a direct path to God in order to create. It doesn't involve going out and looking for a path. It involves getting still and clearing the path that has always been here.

What did this Look Like for me?

FIRST I made a LIST of all the PEOPLE, PLACES, & institutions that had WRONGED ME in some way & the specific resentments I was holding towards them. Before Letting GO of my victimhood, I had to SEE it clearly and let myself embody it fuLLy ...

I am ~~TOP SECRET~~ sentful towards my doctor who wouldn't ~~think~~ me to a nutritionist because "my BMI was fine."
I am resentful towards hormonal birth control for making me gain weight & triggering my eating disorder. I'm resentful towards my eating disorder for taking so much of my energy. I'm resentful towards my ex-boyfriend for cheating on me and lying about it for a year. I am resentful towards my dad for becoming an evangelical Christian out of nowhere and saying things like "There's only one Right!" to try to convince me my life choices were wrong. I'm resentful towards my mom for hating her body and never asserting herself. I'm resentful towards effortlessly skinny women with fast metabolisms. I am resentful towards Diet Culture for hijacking my brain for 25 ~~DO NOT READ!!!~~ I'm resentful towards every audience me ~~who~~ didn't laugh at my set or told me I was ~~"cute"~~ after a show instead of complimenting my VERY HILARIOUS JOKES. I resent all men... do I need a reason... seems self-explanatory.

NEXT I held a mirror up to my List and saw the part I was playing in each one of my resentments and in my reasons for holding onto them. How was I benefitting from seeing myself as a victim? This wasn't about blaming myself instead of others —it was about looking at my stories through a clearer lens to discover deeper truth.

By blaming my doctor, Diet culture, birth control, and my Mom for my relationship with foods my body, I was benefitting by seeing myself as a helpless child who needed love and attention. Self-pity was my way of giving myself the love I needed. I was selfishly assuming the world should follow my script & I shouldn't have to face challenging circumstances in life—I'm SPECIAL! Even now, I'm using the past tense to distance myself from these unsavory patterns... I blamed my ex-boyfriend for lying about cheating on me, which made me feel superior, like I had "won" the relationship, but truthfully I had been dishonest with him as well by hiding my feelings, secretly believing I'd "convince" or trick him into marrying me, and seeing our relationship & him through my own fantasy lens instead of letting in his truth. Same with my parents! I wanted my dad to be cool with me living my truth, but I wasn't cool with him living his truth. I blamed my mom for passing on her body hatred & people-pleasing tendencies to me, wanting to "fix" her instead of facing myself. I was making myself the victim to feel justifiably miserable and avoid what I was afraid to feel underneath.

wow, you really picked a fancy mirror to face yourself in...

STEP 5

We admitted to God, to ourselves, and to another human being the exact nature of our wrongs.

AKA Tell Marie Kondo what you found in your closet.

I've been hoarding toilet paper rolls & yogurt lids for years in case I ever get into arts and crafts or become a teacher...and I have every email from my high school crush printed out & folded into a shoe box... and these pre-pubescent pants I aspire to fit into one day...

Now that we don't see "wrongs" as wrongs (because we see our behavior through the compassionate lens of objectivity rather than judgment), we share what we've discovered about ourselves with someone we trust who can help us see patterns emerging. I shared my inventory with my sponsor Jodi, who refused to let my perfectionism get in the way of my progress —

"Katie, this list doesn't need to be perfect, you just need to keep moving. Don't worry if you miss something — you will continue this process for the rest of your life." (Spoiler Alert for Step 10!) She always said exactly what I needed to hear.

Seeing the patterns in my behavior was a humbling & illuminating experience. I had been afraid to look at my destructive self-sabotage because I didn't think there was a way to deal with it.   ALL of my attempts to "fix" my flaws had only fueled my perfectionism self-condemnation, & guilt.   I now saw my choice was to continue trying to "fix" my flaws on my own OR ask my Higher Power to remove the coping mechanisms that no longer served me.

For the first time in my life, I experienced the freedom of surrender. As soon as I was willing to see myself clearly, I could see the toxic patterns that were chronically making me miserable. Instead of continuing to nitpick and fix these patterns in secret, I could shine a light on them & surrender them to a power greater than myself. I finally gave up trying to be who my ego wanted me to be and let myself become who I actually was.

Making a list of all the ways I had harmed others was another humbling, heartwrenching, eventually liberating process. I looked at all the ways I'd been sneaking around, trying to get away with looking like a "good person," while not actually living my values— stealing food from roommates, snacking on bulk food items before paying for them at the grocery store, not being honest about my inner world with friends & family, withholding affection from my parents, "forgetting" to pay for the yoga towels I borrowed every week.

How to Make an Amends
(according to my sponsor)

1. Make a Specific Statement of the offending behavior & acknowledge the harm done.

2. Take responsibility for one's actions & ask for forgiveness.

3. Ask "Is there anything else I need to know?" "How can I make this right?"

4. Commit to modifying behavior & actually Change ♡

corrective action, amending behavior is Key ⚷ 🔒

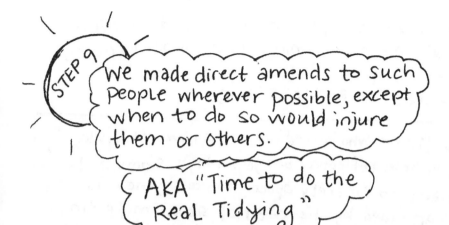

STEP 9

We made direct amends to such people wherever possible, except when to do so would injure them or others.

AKA "Time to do the Real Tidying"

Hey, I want to apologize for holding your tupperware container captive for the past 3 years. I knew it was yours, but I've been using it to transport my lunch to work every day. It is now super smelly & unusable, so I got you a new one! I promise I will not take this long to return things in the future. Is there anything else I need to know about how this affected you or how I can make it right?

Owning up to my actions & taking responsibility for my behavior felt vulnerable and intimidating. My ego was afraid of discomfort & embarrassment, but my heart knew I could trust the process if I approached it with humility & honesty, knowing these were the keys to freedom. My amends included expressing gratitude to mentors I'd harbored resentment against, admitting to my parents when I was acting from a place of arrogance, revealing more of my inner world to close friends & family I'd been hiding from, replacing my roommate's food & printer ink. Each amend I was willing to make planted a seed for a more authentic relationship to Blossom.

Here is an example of an amend I made via E-mail after performing Stand up at a college, where I learned there is a Fine Line Between "relatable" & "triggering."

Dear [person who invited me to perform at his college],

I've been reflecting on yesterday's show and I want to sincerely apologize to anyone who was offended by the material about my eating disorder. My intention was to connect with the audience by speaking openly about something I was once ashamed of. I see that I still have work to do on how I present this material. I did not intend to make light of eating disorders. I was a silent prisoner of bulimia, bingeing & restricting for many years and my intention is to shine a light on my story to help others who suffer feel less alone.

I'm grateful for the humbling reminder that every time I stand in front of an audience, I start from scratch. It doesn't matter how many people have laughed at a joke before, if it isn't working in the moment, it is my job to find the gap and bridge it. I cannot go back and change what happened, but I would like to help make this right. I would be happy to talk to anyone who felt offended or triggered and I'm open to any suggestions you have about repairing the situation.

This experience has reminded me that comedy is about human connection & empathy. Thank you for the opportunity to perform.

Sincerely, Katie

Most people responded to my amends with open hearts, but a

Key component of the amends process (and Life) is Letting Go of attachment to a certain outcome.

Step 10 is about continuing to live in a conscious way and working steps 4-9 whenever they come up in real time. It's not about doing recovery "perfectly" or beating yourself up for moments of "untidiness." Rather, it's a daily check-in with myself & my higher power about any fear, dishonesty, selfishness, or general stickiness that may be present in my thoughts or actions. Taking regular inventory is helpful because those thoughts & feelings fester the longer they go unseen, or unacknowledged.

We sought through prayer and meditation to improve our conscious contact with God as we understood God, praying only for Knowledge of God's will for us and the power to carry that out.

AKA: "What would Marie Kondo do?"

I've developed practices that support my internal tidiness...which is in turn reflected in my external tidiness!

My "Artist's Way" - inspired daily practice of writing stream of consciousness Morning Pages became a way for me to connect to my Higher Power. Writing freely helped me pause, pray, and ask God what my next right action was. I always feel the difference when I am not actively connecting with this higher consciousness daily. I putter around my life anxiously until something reminds me — "Oh, right! God!"

STEP 12

Having had a spiritual awakening as the result of these steps, we tried to carry this message to others [compulsive eaters, addicts, alcoholics, insert whatever resonates with you] and to practice these principles in all our affairs.

AKA "Be the Marie Kondo you want to see in the world."

Hey! How'd your life get so tidy?? What's your secret??

The secret is not having any secrets! I'd be happy to tell you what worked for me.

I only get to keep what I am willing to give away. This step is NOT about forcing the steps down anyone's throat. (I sincerely hope you do not feel they have been forced down yours.) It is about willingness to be of service. It is more important to me to be open about my story in hopes it might help even one person feel less alone than it is to be seen as "having it all figured out." The truth is that I am grateful to have struggled with food my whole life because it led me to a place of freedom I did not even know was possible.

TRUTH GOGGLES $Priceless

Working the Steps with Jodi helped me start seeing my Life through a brand new pair of Truth Goggles.

I continued to check in with myself regularly, asking how I *actually* felt throughout the day & noticing fears, resentments & dishonesty that would crop up.

I did things that felt scary:
- Signed up to retake an improv class that I hadn't passed the first time.
- Ended a professional relationship that wasn't healthy for me
- Planned and performed in a stand up TOUR

Dating became a new arena in which to Live my Truth.

"I don't feel a Romantic connection with you."

This line would have felt impossible to say months prior, for fear of "hurting" someone, but the more I spoke my Real Feelings honestly, the more refreshing my interactions became. It wasn't just about building trust with other people, it was about building trust with myself — trusting myself not to abandon my own boundaries, feelings, & desires to meet someone else's.

RECOVERY Time Capsule

♡ March 17, 2017 ♡

I'm learning that being awake & alive in my life means feeling my pain and joy more deeply. Glennon Doyle said (on Elizabeth Gilbert's 'Magic Lessons' podcast), "It's not the pain that brings us down, it's the shame around the pain." So much of my life has been spent hiding the darker parts of myself, feeling quietly broken, emerging only when I could connect to a Lightness. I was doing it backwards. It's not about Mastering pain, controlling it; it's about sitting with it, accepting it as I would accept snow on the ground. I loved this quote by Kahlil Gibran that was at the end of yoga yesterday (Oh - it's a whole POEM - I'll put it on the next page!).

My intention for the day is to listen to the voice inside of me nudging me towards honesty and truth. I spent so much time trying to make my life sound "good" — now I just want to be honest. I want my life to be real — I want to tell myself the truth, which includes the pain, disappointments, uncertainty of being alive. It also contains great Joy & Simplicity. Breathing into this life. ♥

On Pain

Kahlil Gibran
1883-1931

And a Woman spoke, saying, Tell us of Pain.
And he said:

Your pain is the breaking of the shell that encloses your understanding.

Even as the stone of the fruit must break, that its heart may stand in the sun, so you must know Pain.

And could you keep your heart in wonder at the daily miracles of your life your pain would not seem less wondrous than your joy.

And you would accept the seasons of your heart, even as you have always accepted the seasons that pass over your fields.

And you would watch with serenity through the winters of your grief.

Much of your pain is self-chosen.

It is the bitter **potion** by which the physician within you heals your sick self.

Therefore trust the physician, and drink his remedy in silence and tranquility:

For his hand, though heavy and hard, is guided by the tender hand of the Unseen,

And the cup he brings, though it burn your lips, has been fashioned of the clay which the Potter has moistened with His own sacred tears.

♡ March 24, 2017 ♡

One of my game-changing moments was realizing I am just as much of a person as anyone else. The people who are thriving and living fulfilled, happy lives deserve all the space they take up, and so do the people who are struggling in survival mode. I am also worthy of the space I take up. I am learning how to stand in it, spread out, meet people in their space while not feeling threatened by their space. I want my being to extend out to my surface.

I've been keeping my full self hidden under smiles, under what I think I should be, taking up less than my whole space. I've been aware of this & in that awareness I have mistakenly grabbed for opportunities, seeking frantically to expand my space. It is right here though. The space I need is contained within the limits of my body. Bodies were built to carry our infinite spirits. You are afraid of losing something you cannot lose. Breathe, be in your body. Come alive by being intensely where you are. This is your space. This is your home. Keep it warm, inviting - welcome others in. There is room for all of us in this life. Surround yourself with people who have learned to take up their own space, who don't feel the need to chronically encroach on yours. The expansive life you're craving exists within you. ♥

I feel the desire to WARN YOU the story gets a wee bit dark here. I think it's funny I want to somehow caution or protect you when I just spent a whole book saying things like "welcome the darkness" and "trust that other people can handle your truth." That being said, you've been warned ♥

Three months after starting our work together, Jodi passed away suddenly & inexplicably. Shock. Denial. Anger. More shock. Acceptance. They all came on at once and again in waves. I could feel the feelings bubble up & down and was also aware of their inevitable resolution. No one who knew me like Jodi knew me had ever died. It felt like a piece of me was dying too. Her voice in my head continued to guide me: "The best thing you can do is recover yourself."

Miraculously I didn't turn to bingeing or restricting or alcohol. I was confused and devastated, but also connected to my Higher Power more than ever. I trusted, on the deepest level, that in as much as Jodi's passing affected me, it had to be a welcome part of my journey. Resisting was pointless. "This must be the 'surrendering to God's will' thing I've heard so much about," I thought to myself.

I had never met Jodi in person (we had only worked over the phone), but she saved my life.

Her family generously opened up her visitation to the public, and I felt compelled to go.

I showed up at the Funeral Home reception Hall in the Middle of Nowhere, knowing no one, watching a sea of sad strangers connect with each other. I wondered who her ex-husband might be. Her kids. I spoke to a fellow solo straggler and probably talked more than I listened, as I can't remember anything about who they were. I saw the casket in the corner of the room. Was this the reason I was here? To see Jodi's body for the first time?

The whole thing felt like a dream, coloring in details of a life I knew nothing about. I approached the casket, bracing myself for I didn't know what.

HELLO
my name is

[one of the countless anonymous souls Jodi has touched♥]

Looking at her lying there was surreal. It was like she was an unplugged animatronic 3-D version of her Facebook profile picture. Something you'd find in a wax museum. I had experienced her soul and her spirit and they were not here at all. I stood there thinking about how one day I would write about this moment, meeting this woman who had struggled for years with bulimia, restricting, alcoholism, hating her body — meeting her only _as_ a body, the thing she felt so disconnected from, oddly gave me a sense of permission to take my own body less seriously. These flesh puppets we live in are nothing without the animation of our spirit, yet they are also vitally important. Here I was meeting Jodi's flesh puppet with no Jodi inside. These bodies are temporary, but necessary — helpful even. They are mobile soul homes we get to inhabit for a short time. This body is my home but it is not who I am. It is the costume of the character I am playing in this lifetime.

As I stood there, weeping & pondering, a wise-beyond her years middle schooler approached me.

At first, I thought it must have been another Katie because we had naturally transitioned to daily texts instead of calls, but looking back, I know this reminder must have been from those first few days and weeks of my recovery when she was there with me every night—ready to read with me, to listen to me, help me over the hurdle of self-obsessed fear into the freedom of recovery. I loved the thought that this once vital reminder had become a daily prod she would routinely snooze, modify, or ignore, like I do with so many "reminders" that weave themselves into the rhythm of my life. Perhaps the reminder was only there to give her daughter this memory to relay, reminding me of Jodi's unrelenting commitment to her recovery and to mine. Even though she was gone, she was showing me how to love and honor myself more intentionally—I could set my own "Call Katie" reminder, check in with myself. "How are you?" "How are you really?" "What secret thoughts and feelings are you having?" "What are you grateful for today?"

I met Jodi through her daughter more than I met her through her body.

She was a no-bullshit young woman who held space for my emotions with her presence, like a strong structure with pores. Like a rock with holes in it. A coral reef you could say.

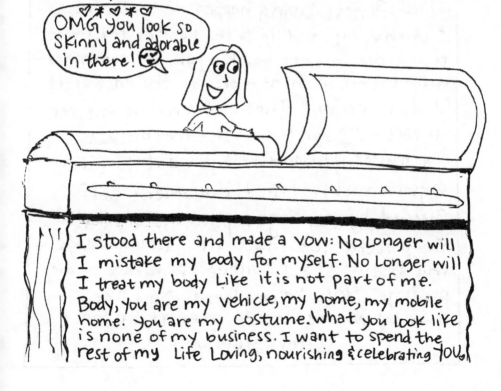

Looking back at Jodi's body once more, I noticed how tiny she was and how cute her Lululemon track jacket looked on her petite frame. I laughed at the ridiculousness of how these would have been ideal compliments to receive at one point in our lives.

OMG you look so skinny and adorable in there!

I stood there and made a vow: No Longer will I mistake my body for myself. No Longer will I treat my body Like it is not part of me. Body, you are my vehicle, my home, my mobile home. You are my costume. What you look like is none of my business. I want to spend the rest of my Life Loving, nourishing & celebrating YOU.

RECOVERY Time Capsule

So good!

♡March 25, 2017♡

LOVE Warrior by Glennon Doyle

I just finished reading "Love Warrior" by Glennon Doyle and I feel a tingly sense of hope, fear, and belonging — vulnerability. I belong here. I am worthy of love. I want to live at the surface of my body. That is the only way I will ever truly be known and loved. Life isn't about protecting myself from pain, it's about staying present and alive through it, letting it galvanize and change me. Maybe this is what "The Alchemist" will be about.

The Alchemist by Paulo Coelho ♡

Spoiler Alert? I've read it before, but not through the lens I have now. Honest living happens in real time. I often want to flip to the back of the book to find the answers, but they are all contained within this moment — even if the answer is "I don't know." That's often the answer in fact — "I don't know, let me consult my trusted advisor, God!" I want to trust myself more, my in-the-moment self guided by my higher power. I am feeling so grateful for my life. Being inside my body is a privilege... priniledge... nope, privilege. You belong here. You are exactly where you're meant to be.

I love you ♡

♥APRIL 1, 2017♥

It is misleading to simply say "I am worthy of Love." Living whole heartedly also means saying "I am worthy of Pain." I am fully invested in the experience of being human. I am not happy all the time; I am not sad all the time — but I can hope to be awake and alive in my life all the time. I don't care about being "happy", I just want to be awake, (which is its own kind of happiness — a blissful awareness). You are HERE.

At any moment, you can wake up and say "I am here." Slowly, you string moments together where this knowing exists within you. "I am here." And that's how you stay alive, awake.

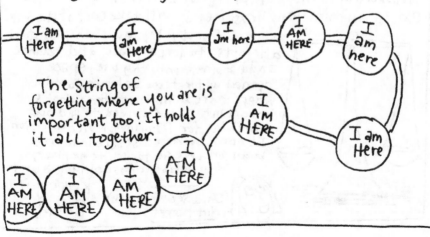

The string of forgetting where you are is important too! It holds it all together.

♡ APRIL 2, 2017 ♡

I lived so much of my life as a scientist, a pharmacist trying to concoct the perfect elixir of happiness, the right balance of food and coffee and weight and sweat and exercise and bottomless mimosas. I kept adding more to each side of the scale, and in certain moments, balance was achieved, making me believe I was "in control."

As you can see, I live a very balanced life!

Little did I know, the substances and activities I was using to compulsively balance my life were blocking me from my Higher Power, who was patiently whispering to me, "Take it all off. The balance exists within you. Trust me. I will take care of the scale."

When I finally let go of my constant attempts to force peace and balance and happiness into my life, space opened up for true balance to exist, where there's only room for what's important. I don't need to go out searching for pain, love, joy, connection. It comes when I settle into my body and we go forth together, seeing, listening, doing as a unit. Keeping it Simple.

Oh, I see what you did there!

"This isn't about me," Jodi would often remind me as I thanked her profusely for taking me through the steps and changing my life. "I'm only here to put your hand in your Higher Power's hand." And that's exactly what she did. I began to feel new levels of closeness with the people in my life who I'd never before let so fully into my experience. I could feel when my actions were coming from my will or God's guidance.

"MY will is what I think should
      be happening;
God's will is what is actually
      happening." – Someone in a
                       Meeting once

I was also following my nutritionist's meal plan, which brought me PEACE around food. I was taking responsibility for myself, bringing containers of Stir Fries & Salads & yogurt parfaits to parties & shows instead of skipping meals and bingeing on whatever I could find later. The peace I felt wasn't about the food, but the FREEDOM that came with not obsessing about food. Suddenly SPACE opened up that let me focus on Participating in my LIFE ♡

Chapter 7
Intuitive
Eating

AKA
Throw Away The Tasteless
Diet Food you've Been Pretending
to Enjoy & Order a Burrito

JUST THE WAY YOU LIKE IT ♡

Salsa on the Side Please!

You have permission to enjoy this!

My mom's question hit my tender heart in just the right spot — what WOULD be so bad about getting fat? Despite all the healing I'd done, it was clear I was still acting out of FEAR of fatness on some level. Following a nutritionist's mealplan while working the steps was exactly what I needed to STOP focusing on food & focus on my inner experience instead, but now I was beginning to see that I was relying on the meal plan out of fear. Who would I be without it?

 Mom's comment came about 6 months after Jodi died. I was feeling LOST, insecure, and ungrounded.

I was hesitant about getting a new sponsor in OA because I could feel myself becoming attached to the 12-Step method of awakening and I was curious about what else might help me grow & expand. Something inside of me said that more

FREEDOM and SELF-TRUST were possible.

"I felt guilty admitting this to myself – was I betraying the program?? Was I betraying my Higher Power?! Did God want me to weigh & measure my sugarless, flourless meals for all of eternity?! Was I trying to be sneaky and "take my Will back" instead of following God's Will??

When I heard about Intuitive Eating, lightbulbs went off in my head and heart.

Intuitive Eating is about re-cultivating SELF-TRUST. My Higher Power LOVES it when I trust myself!

My PERSONAL JOURNEY back to Intuitive Eating was Long & Circuitous, much Like my entire recovery Journey. With each new Layer of Discovery I was BLOWN away that there was even MORE to Learn (and UnLearn).

Start here →

I was BORN an Intuitive Eater."

↑ ...Allegedly. I have no memory of this.

I wanted to diet just like Mom & felt Guilt eating certain foods.

Downloaded a Diet app & fulfilled my Dieting Dreams! I LOST weight!

When it was time to enter a "maintenance" phase, I took a sharp Left Turn Towards...

OBSESSION: Food & Exercise Became only NUMBERS to me.

But REALLY doing it for weight loss ↓

Dabbled in Orthorexia – going Gluten Free & vegetarian in the name of "Health"

Also coinciding with a traumatic Breakup & starting hormonal birth control →

Restricting led to Bingeing which led to BULIMIA.

I genuinely wanted to eat in a more balanced way, but didn't Know HOW.

Which was intellectually true... but I didn't trust my "knowing" on a body Level.

Started working with a nutritionist who told me, "It sounds Like you already Know how & what to eat."

Joined Overeaters Anonymous where I defined my bottom Line abstinence as "no purging."

Had a binge & purge relapse over the Holidays after 7 months of abstinence.

Surrendered to working with a sponsor and a nutritionist who gave me a specific meal plan to follow.

Following this meal plan opened my eyes to how much food my body needed.

My period disappeared and I eventually realized I was tricking my nutritionist by Lying about what a "comfortable" weight was for me

I found the Book "Intuitive Eating" by Evelyn Tribole & ELyse Resch and set out to make Peace with Food

I had a feeling my meal plan was restrictive and perhaps MORE FREEDOM was possible →

Enter the Portal of Intuitive Eating...

↖ Also: coincided with quitting drinking alcohol.

The next several pages will outline

The Ten Principles

from the book

"Intuitive Eating"

by Evelyn Tribole & Elyse Resch

Based on how I *personally* understand and implement them.

Principles Preview:

1. Reject the Diet Mentality
2. Honor your Hunger
3. Make Peace with Food.
4. Challenge the Food Police
5. Feel your Fullness
6. Discover the Satisfaction Factor
7. Cope with Emotions
8. Respect your body
9. Exercise: Feel the difference
10. Honor your Health with Gentle Nutrition.

If you read this and Intuitive Eating (IE) sounds aligned for you, I highly recommend Buying the Book! My intention is to give you a Katie-flavored appetizer, but this is not meant to replace the book and/or working with a Non-Diet, IE dietitian. AKA I'm reiterating my Disclaimer that this is meant to be ART, not clinical advice... even when it sounds like I'm giving clinical advice.

Intuitive Eating Principle #1

Reject the DIET MENTALITY

AKA

UN-BRAINWASH

yourself from the

CULT* of Diet Culture

* CULT: (n)
a group of people devoted to an idea or movement that becomes detrimental when the people are not there by **conscious choice** ♡

Being a Grown-Up
means getting to choose What you are BRAINWASHED by

In the same way that surrounding myself with Diet-Culture emboldened my "Diet-culture-informed" beliefs, surrounding myself with "Anti-Diet Culture" helped me build NEW "Anti-Diet" & "Intuitive Eating" beliefs. Once I saw the toxic ideas I'd been influenced by, I CHOSE to make a conscious pivot towards new ideas that felt more supportive, loving, and aligned with my values.

Here are some resources that helped me personally reject the Diet Mentality:

→ more in the Back of the BOOK ♥

Christy Harrison's MPH, RD

↓ BOOK called "Anti-Diet" Loaded with Evidence about the Roots of diet culture & how Dieting does not WORK & is a TOOL of OPPRESSION.

↓ Podcast called "Food Psych," which introduced me to a diverse group of Body Positive, anti-diet influencers AND

Intuitive Eating & Non-Diet Dieticians, which I followed on social Media, Replacing my "FITSPO" FEED.

The Book "Intuitive Eating," (which I'm summarizing now that is LOADED with evidence that Diets are ineffective and Harmful to Health.

The "Health at Every Size" (HAES) approach.

Hang on... Health at EVERY size??
Surely SOME sizes cannot be healthy.
Are you promoting OBESITY?!
ARE YOU PROMOTING Disease??
Surely we MUST continue to
Shame people at higher weights so
they don't get too comfortable with
their bodies and maybe live a
Happy, Healthy Life at whatever
size they are! ...oh wait.

P.S.A.: SHAME is not an effective Weight Loss TOOL.

"Health at Every Size" promotes a weight-neutral approach to health. In the Western world, people in larger bodies are assumed to be "unhealthy," which is a form of WEIGHT STIGMA.

Ironically, weight stigma itself, including the STRESS of "needing to lose weight to be healthy" leads to Negative Health outcomes. DISEASE (dis-ease) comes from a Lack of EASE in the Body.

♡ EVERYONE will be healthier if we stop using weight as an indicator of health and start letting Bodies Be Bodies at whatever size or shape they are. ♡

Diet culture gives us permission to hate ourselves in a way that feels Productive.

Trying to change our bodies might make us feel like we're working towards a goal, but really we're on a hamster wheel of Dieting Doom.

Dieting is like any addiction, distracting us from the unpleasant feelings we'd like to avoid. This coping mechanism has helped us SURVIVE by numbing intense emotions — there's no shame in having used it. But when we see what's happening more clearly, we get to decide if we want to continue living under the illusion or face what's underneath.

Intuitive Eating Principle #2 — HONOR your HUNGER

Are you there, hunger? It's me, Margaret.

I Learned that There are many TYPES of Hunger:

Biological Hunger

"Please put food in me, I need it to do Stuff!"
— Body

TASTE Hunger

"Mmm, a cookie would be Yummy after dinner."
— Taste Buds

"Practical Hunger"

"I won't have a chance to eat dinner Later, so I'll eat now while I'm able to."
— Mind

Emotional Hunger

"I want some comfort and this hot chocolate Sounds comforting to me."
— Heart

... and aLL types are valid ♡

After Spending months, years, or Lifetimes overriding the body's natural Signals for hunger, we can begin to Regain the Body's TRust by Listening & Responding to its hunger cues.

Dear Body,
I hereby grant you unconditionaL permission to eat food and I promise to stop bossing you around as if I Know better than you. My new dieting tool is tuning into YOU, so I'm here whenever you're ready to talk to me again. Love, Me

Intuitive Eating Principle #3: Make Peace with Food

⇨ Feeling Obsessed with and out-of-control around FOOD stems directly from Physical and/or Psychological Deprivation.

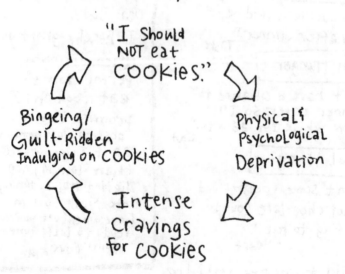

"I should NOT eat cookies."

Physical & Psychological Deprivation

Intense cravings for cookies

Bingeing/Guilt-Ridden Indulging on cookies

When my body thinks it will no longer have access to a particular food, cravings for that food can become intense. The forbidden food takes on a sexy, alluring, naughty quality.

There are TWO WAYS to Eliminate
Guilty Pleasures

1. Remove the PLEASURE

or

2. Remove the GUILT

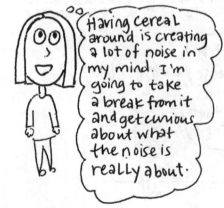

Giving myself **Unconditional Permission to Eat What I Want**

was my Ticket out of the Deprivation → Bingeing → Restricting CYCLE of DOOM.

It is also the MOST TERRIFYING concept imaginable to Someone* who has spent their entire life convinced there were "good" & "bad" foods and one must avoid the "bad" foods at all costs so as to not have a "binge my brains out" episode. [*me!]

When I truly believe
I have PERMISSION to do Something,
actually doing that thing becomes
a CONSCIOUS choice
rather than an
unconscious compulsion ♥

I tell my Inner Child, "I will Love
you no matter what you eat or what
Size you are. What else does your
heart need to feel permission for?"

The process of "Making Peace with food" can Look Like this:

1. Pay attention to & make a List of Foods that sound <u>appealing</u>.

2. Circle any foods that have been <u>Forbidden</u>

3. Pick one "Forbidden Food" to try by buying it at the store or ordering at a restaurant.

4. Check in with yourself about whether or not you *ACTUALLY* like it.

5. If you do Like it, continue to give yourself permission to eat it! Keep it in your pantry and/or order it as often as you Like.

6. Repeat steps 3-5 for all Forbidden Foods, or until you finally trust you <u>DO</u> have permission to eat all foods♡

It's okay— I'm a Friendly cookie!

My first experience allowing myself to eat a forbidden food was when I was gifted a pair of French macarons at a café after I found a hair in my food. (score!) I wasn't hungry at the time, so I took them home with me and had a standoff with them all afternoon. I hadn't been eating refined sugar for the previous 8 months, but the principles of Intuitive Eating resonated with me and I knew I wanted to explore this Forbidden Food in a safe space. I sat down with some tea and the chocolate macaron, unsure of whether my world would end or expand. I took a bite. "WOW! Sugar! Sweet! Okay what does this mean?! I like macarons! I'll keep eating this and let myself buy more in the future!" Approaching the cookie with the intention of making peace & cultivating self-trust helped me be intensely present, slowing down time enough to hear my inner voice ♡

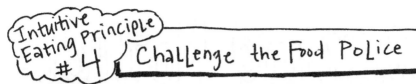

Intuitive Eating Principle #4 | Challenge the Food Police

AKA Shine a LIGHT on all the TOXIC Diet-Culture beliefs that have implanted themselves into my subconscious brain...

I'm "good" if I eat less food.

I'm "Bad" if I eat sugar.

Bread is the devil.

I'll have to make up for this tomorrow.

I already ruined the day by eating ... I might as well eat everything else in my house.

Oh, I get it! When I observe these thoughts from this angle, I can see they arent me, they're the FOOD Police!

Casting Notice!

Recasting for the Role of: The Voice in my Head

TYPE: Nurturing, Honest, Accepting

Description: Delivers helpful insights in a calm, loving, often humorous manner; HIGHLY COMPATIBLE With Protagonist.

Delightful & Deep. Gives authentic compliments

Genre: Dark comedy

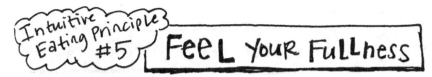

FeeL YouR FuLLness

FuLL (ness) DiscLosure:

This is **still** the most challenging principle for me.

After years of overriding my body's hunger cues, I needed to rebuild trust that it was SAFE to STOP eating at the point of fullness, knowing I would feed myself again when I got hungry. My body was accustomed to operating in Starvation Mode as a Default.

When my #1 Priority was "Shrinking my Body," it didn't even occur to me to pay attention to what I actually liked. I walked around with the assumption "What I like is bad for me"—I never considered it might be the KEY to feeling balanced and at peace in my body. Not only can I eat whatever I want, I get to choose foods and eating experiences I LIKE.

The first step to doing this involved getting Curious:

WHat do I *actually* Like?

What do I actually Like??

Intuitive Eating encourages me to become the playful anthropologist of my eating experience — noticing how my tastebuds, mouth, body, mind respond to various eating experiences. What sensual experience am I in the mood for?

IS the APPEARANCE of this food appealing to my eyes? Does it look fresh, yummy, intriguing?

What aroma is appealing to me? Do I like the smell of this food while it cooks?

What TEXTURES would feel satisfying right now? Creamy, crunchy, chewy, smooth, lumpy?

What TASTE do I want in here? Salty, sweet, spicy, sour, bitter?

What TEMPERATURE am I attracted to? Do I like hot soup on a cold day, ice cream in the rain, room temperature pizza?

How FILLING do I want my food to be right now? Am I in the mood for something dense & heavy or light & airy? What will feel satisfying in my stomach?

Check-in with myself Before, during & after meals ♡
☑ ☑ ☑

Hot tips

THESE are NOT meant to be Rules!

for making your

Eating Experience more Enjoyable

(courtesy of "Intuitive Eating", the Book)

Savor your Food

Like you're sitting in a French café

- Give yourself Time to eat & Sit down
- Take Deep breaths before eating to Calm & focus
- Eat SLOWLY & taste each bite that enters your mouth
- Put your fork down once in a while
- Check-in with your fullness

Eat when GENTLY hungry rather than Over-Hungry

So that your body can be in Satisfaction mode rather than Survival Mode ♡

Eat in a Pleasant environment ♡

Set up your eating space Like you would for a guest you adore ♡

Avoid Emotionally-Charged Talks While Eating —

they are distracting and disappointing when you realize all your food has been eaten without enjoyment.

Keep a Variety of Food in the Home

Having a Lack of appealing food choices can lead to a sense of Deprivation. Keeping a well-stocked supply of Yummy items will encourage satisfying food choices ♡

A few friendly
Reminders from
the Universe:

You have permission to have NON-satisfying food experiences and still be an intuitive eater. You have permission to eat things that taste good to you. You have permission to eat things just because they're there. You have permission to stop eating when something doesn't taste good. You have permission to keep eating when something doesn't taste good. You have permission to grant yourself more and more permission as new thoughts of "I'm doing this wrong" arise.

"Doing this wrong" doesn't even EXIST. You are permanently DOING THIS RIGHT♥

Intuitive Eating Principle #7 — Cope with your Emotions without using food.

↖ And with using food if you want! This is more about increasing conscious awareness around food behavior so it becomes a __Choice__ rather than a Compulsion ♡

Ooo! What's in the Present?!

To: You
From: Your Emotional Body

Wanting to Eat when I'm not BioLogicaLLy HungRy is a Gift — it's a treasure map that Leads me to feelings that want to be felt & needs that want to be met.
♥

Friendly Reminder from the Universe: You haven't done anything Wrong ♡

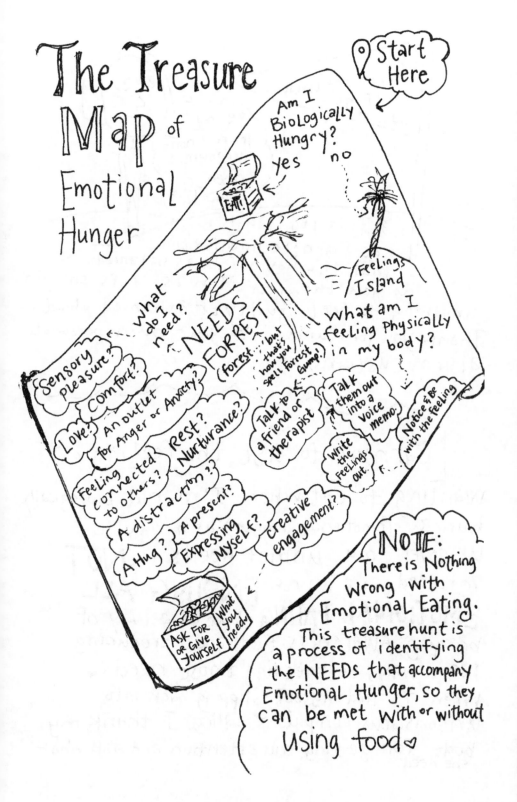

Learning to use the feeling of wanting to eat when I'm not biologically hungry (emotional hunger) as a way to uncover my unmet needs is NOT intended as a way of ENDING ALL EMOTIONAL EATING, but as a way of bringing AWARENESS to it, and introducing new ways of meeting those needs. When I find myself slipping back into unconscious compulsive eating, I thank my body for getting my attention and ask what she needs.

I noticed I would often turn to a jar of peanut butter when I encountered a "difficult" problem in Life (Like sending a stressful E-maiL... difficulty can be relative!)

What am I doing?! I don't need to be eating peanut butter right now, I'm not hungry.

Ohh...that's right, I'm avoiding a nagging task.

It seems like I just wanted to take a break.

Eating peanut butter straight from the jar with my fingers helps me think.

Is this what meditating feels like? I bet this is what meditating feels like.

Learning to be a non-judgmental observer of my thoughts & actions, helped me understand what my actuaL needs were underneath my compulsive eating behaviors.

keyword

{Now} when I notice myself eating when I'm not hungry, sometimes I remember to use that moment as a portal to my inner truth, as Geneen Roth beautifully describes in her book, "Women, Food, & God."

00:05:00
Til you can eat that thing

First, I set a timer for myself, making a deal with my body that she can eat whatever she wants after going through this process (the point is not to eliminate emotional eating, simply to bring awareness to it).

Then I lie on the floor, place my hands wherever they want to go on my body, and gently, with genuine curiosity, ask....

What are you REALLY hungry for?

...then listen for the answer, trusting whatever I hear is right ♡

I'm hungry for you to stop putting so much pressure on me!

I'm hungry to feel heard, held, and loved.

I'm hungry for excitement & risk... I'm bored & looking for something to do.

I'm hungry for some sweetness, which is okay to get from food, but I also want it from life!

Intuitive Eating Principle #8 — Respect Your Body

... duh.

...but also not-so duh.

I love that this principle is about **Respecting** the body rather than "Loving" it. Loving your body is great too of course, but the command "Love Your Body" can lead me to shaming myself into inauthentically pretending to love my body because I think it's what I "Should" do.

o Authenticity is the key

Finding **authentic** gratitude and **acceptance** for my body was a good place to start. After a lifetime of conditioning telling me to blame & hate my appearance, I wasn't able to jump straight into saying,

"I LOVE MY BODY UNCONDITIONALLY."

Instead, I focus on what Gratitude feels REAL & TRUE for me in the moment:

I wish I were more grateful for my body.

I want to nourish and care for my body exactly as it is now, without trying to change it.

My body is the exact shape & size it needs to be at all times.

My body has been resilient through years of struggle.

205

The "Intuitive Eating" Guide to Respecting Your BODY

Basic Tenets:

- [ ] my body deserves to move comfortably
- [ ] my body deserves to be dressed comfortably in a style I enjoy
- [ ] my body deserves to be touched affectionately and with Respect.
- [ ] my body deserves to be fed.
- [ ] my body deserves to be treated with dignity

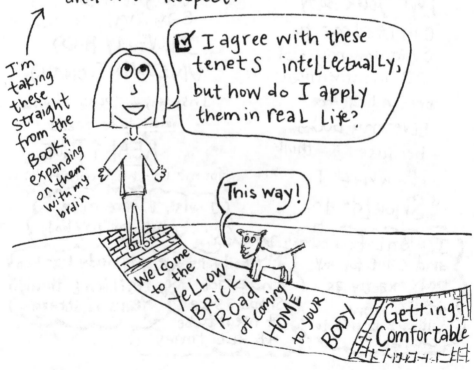

I'm taking these straight from the BOOK & expanding on them with my brain

- [x] I agree with these tenets intellectually, but how do I apply them in real life?

This way!

Welcome to the Yellow Brick Road of coming Home to your BODY

Getting Comfortable

Getting Comfortable

I'm going to sign up for this expensive weight loss plan so I can fit into my underwear again.

Why don't you just buy new underwear?

For years I wouldn't let myself go shopping for clothes unless I was at the low end of my weight spectrum. This meant all of my fun, cute clothes only fit me properly when I was a smaller size. Gaining weight not only bummed me out numbers-wise, but also meant I had to wear clothes that compounded my low self-worth. My aspirational wardrobe didn't motivate me as much as it made me feel bad about myself every time a waistband tugged too tight or a jacket refused to button. The truth is, we deserve to be comfortable in our bodies here & now.

BUY CLOTHES YOU LIKE & Underwear that fits♡

Stop Weighing Yourself

And using other arbitrary external measures to evaluate your self worth

These pants won't zip. Something must be wrong with me. I'm too BIG!

Maybe nothing is wrong with YOU. Something's wrong with your pants. They're too tight!

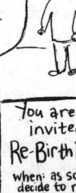

I wonder if it's environmentally inconsiderate to host a scale-burning party.

HELL-OMeter

You are cordially invited to your Re-Birth Day Party!

When: as soon as you decide to reclaim your life from dieting

Where: Right HERE

What: PotLuck! Please bring a dish you actually like & any scales, aspirational "skinny" pants, & self-doubt you want to destroy ♡

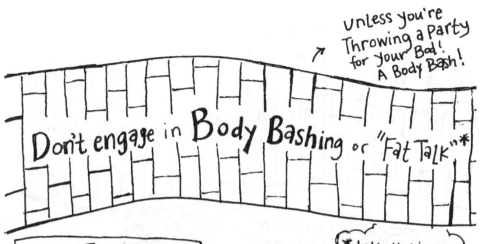

Unless you're Throwing a party for your Bod! A Body Bash!

Don't engage in Body Bashing or "Fat Talk"*

Not so **Fun Fact:** when you judge yourself for something OR hold yourself to an abusively high standard, you are ALSO judging others and holding them to **abusively high standards** ♥

The First Step to Stopping "Body Bashing" (or any behavior) is to become aware of when & how you are engaging in the behavior.

*talk that implies fatness is a bad thing, AKA Fat Phobic Talk

Actual **Fun Fact:**
What you FOCUS your attention on GROWS. If you keep focusing on areas of your body you dislike — these will be the Main parts of yourself you notice. If you FOCUS on parts of your body you do Like, these WILL be the parts you notice. It makes looking in the mirror SO MUCH BETTER.

My Internal Monologue

Actual →

Ugh, I hate my double chin, backfat, tummy, thighs, arm jiggle, [insert body feature of choice]

I wish I looked like "x." I wonder what "x" eats

How did "y" get so fit?! I'm not doing enough.

FEED ME! what am I supposed to be doing right now?

Oh I'm Hungry! NO! I am I

Ideal →

What am I seeing, hearing, smelling, feeling, tasting, doing in this moment? What do I love about right NOW?

Respect Body Diversity, Especially Yours

Bodies are like trees— every single one is Beautiful exactly as it is. But I still want to be the skinniest Palm Tree on the Block.

It's not a competition. Humans— am I right?

This is a good time to...

Acknowledge your Internalized Fat Phobia

But I would NEVER judge someone ELSE for their body size or appearance, only myself.

That's what we mean by "internalized". It's just as toxic!

You might want to try surrounding yourself with more body diversity in your friend group and/or people you follow on social media.

Do nice things for your Body

Instead of forcing your body to maintain a weight it can only sustain by eating rice cakes (aka crunchy air) and cucumbers, treat your body to PLeasurable Experiences ♥

Take a Bath with things that smell nice.

Buy a Lotion you Love ♥

Get a massage or facial.

Go to a Sauna or Whirlpool

Lie in the Grass ☼

Ask a friend to exchange back/ neck rubs ♥

Eat food you enjoy ♥

Insert any Body-Love activities that sound nice to you

BMI: (n.) Bullshit Misery Index;

an imprecise measuring tool that gives zero information about a person's body composition and cannot accurately predict health outcomes. "Many researchers...have recommended that BMI be discarded as an outdated and ineffective tool for measuring health." —Christy Harrison in *Anti-Diet*

↑
I've said it once and I'll say it again...Read This Book! 🔥
↑
(fire)

"Set Point" Weight Range:

Our bodies have a natural, genetically programmed weight range they can <u>comfortably</u> maintain. This range may shift throughout the life span—including as a reaction to chronic dieting (this may cause the set point to increase to protect the body from perceived famine). When the body goes below this set point, it freaks out, triggering a period of bingeing for survival.

Healing comes from Neutralizing

our weight & size, accepting our Natural state as we accept our height, hair color, hand size, eye color, earlobe shape, etc.

Exercise – Feel the Difference

Actual Alarm I used to set on my phone.

Wake up and WORKOUT, You Walki Tub of Lard

SNOOZE

Since my relationship with exercise was Predominantly Punitive, aka with the main intention of "Weight loss," it was important to take a step back and Listen to how my body actually __wanted__ to move.

Movement: (n) akin to exercise, except I actually WANT to do it

Mobilizing

Our

Vehicles (bodies)

enjoyably.

Maybe

ecstatically!

Not

too much.

To Run or Not to Run:

A Blog Post I Wrote in the Throes of Recovery

I woke up with a strong urge to weigh myself this morning. This instinct crops up whenever I think my weight will be especially low (like after taking a giant poop or doing a Bikram yoga class) or high (like after eating chocolate chip pumpkin bread, plantain chips, and Ice cream like I did last night). I'm looking for a reason to justify whatever choice I'm going to make about my day—whether I should go for a run or write first. Of course I want to run because part of my brain is still telling me eating sugar is "bad" and this "bad" girl needs to be punished (cue sexy music ramping up and then a record scratch when we see the punishment is just me doing situps until I want to puke).

Part of what I'm working on with Intuitive Eating (aka the way we were born to eat) is giving myself permission to eat all foods without having to "deserve" them. I don't need to buy into the insane equation in my brain: "You can eat this pumpkin bread now if you promise to run 5 miles tomorrow and eat nothing but protein shakes and egg whites for a week!" Also, what do I think the number on the scale is going to tell me?! It's like I think I'm a professional wrestler and if I don't make a lower weight class, my whole life and career will come crashing down.

Weighing myself is like shaking a magic 8 ball to decide if I'm worthy of being alive and taking up space. I ask the scale, "Should I run before writing this morning?"

Try again later

To Run or Not To Run (continued)

If the number on the scale is higher than I thought, it means, "Run immediately! Ignore your body's hunger cues! You're not hungry, you're huge!" If it's lower than I thought, "ALSO RUN! You can make this number smaller—but first have another sliver of pumpkin bread to reward yourself! Take a millimeter off the entire perimeter so your roommate doesn't notice any is missing. Okay maybe 2 millimeters. Or 3. Maybe cut off an entire row. OH NO, NOW YOU REALLY HAVE TO RUN!" In either situation, what I'm doing is obsessing over my body and not WRITING. Funny how that works. My obsessive body & food thoughts keep me from Showing Up for Life—taking action, following my creative impulses, expressing my truth. In this moment I can recognize the saboteur voices in my own mind and politely ask them to be quiet. I can ask my body how she feels instead of asking the scale how I should feel. So, how do you feel, body?

"Well, I'm a little sore from yoga yesterday. I am hungry. I would like a scramble with roasted veggies, pesto, and goat cheese please. And an Almond Milk Latte! I would like to eat this at my desk so I can write and look out the window. Oh! And WATER. I AM SO THIRSTY!!! Thank you for checking in!"

I finally understand why people take pictures of their food. For me, this picture means I took care of myself today. I listened to my body and gave her what she was asking for. I'm treating myself with gentleness and compassion. I'm choosing to nourish my body instead of abuse it. I'm also choosing to show up and write this blog post (now book post) instead of falling into the addictive temptation to "go for a run so you'll weigh less!" I'm excited to say I have no idea how much I weigh right now, but I know it's enough for my body to work & function & write this, so I'm at my ideal weight in my book ♥

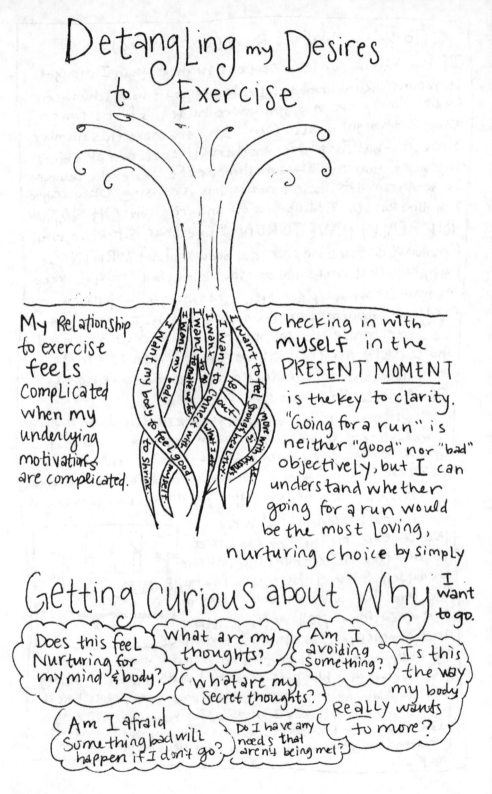

Detangling my Desires to Exercise

I went my body to shrink.
I Went my body to feel good.
I want to make myself.
I want to connect with.
I want to put. What is it?
I want to feel. More tense with.
I want to feel more with my...

My Relationship to exercise feels complicated when my underlying motivations are complicated.

Checking in with myself in the PRESENT MOMENT is the key to clarity. "Going for a run" is neither "good" nor "bad" objectively, but I can understand whether going for a run would be the most loving, nurturing choice by simply

Getting Curious about Why I want to go.

Does this feel Nurturing for my mind & body?

What are my thoughts?

Am I avoiding something?

Is this the way my body REALLY wants to move?

What are my secret thoughts?

Am I afraid something bad will happen if I don't go?

Do I have any needs that aren't being met?

And finally...

Intuitive Eating Principle #10

Honor Your Health with Gentle Nutrition

"We will not be healthier, both psychologically and physically, about our food until we learn to love it more, not less... with a relaxed, generous, unashamed emotion. In the process, it may be that we have to redefine fundamentally the concept of 'eating well.'"

— Michelle Stacey, author of <u>Consumed: Why Americans Love, Hate, & Fear Food</u>

"If a healthy relationship with food is not in place, it is difficult to truly pursue healthy eating." — <u>Intuitive Eating</u>

Orthorexia(n) a rigid obsession with eating "healthily"

I can't be an intuitive eater because I'd eat nothing but pizza and ice cream all day.

Intuitive eating isn't about eating whatever I want and ignoring my body's cues. It's about tuning into what my body REALLY wants & honoring that, knowing that I truly have permission to eat all foods. Some days I want pizza & ice cream & other days I want a hearty salad & green juice. When I started to know in my bones that I didn't need to feel guilty for eating what I wanted, "what I wanted" was able to expand & neutralize.

Much Like Recovery in General,
Intuitive Eating is a Daily Choice
I make to be Present with myself
and my experience. There is no
WRONG way to do it — it is
Simply a commitment to follow
what is TRUE for ME over
what I think *Should* be True for ME.

Sometimes I judge my food choices.

Sometimes I get anxious and don't feed myself enough.

Sometimes I feel disconnected from my body & intuition

Sometimes I get anxious and feed myself "too much."

Sometimes I miss the "in control" feeling Dieting gave me.

Knowing my FEELINGS about food are not REALLY about food allows them to become a doorway to the DEEPER TRUTH underneath.

Chapter 8

Soon after embarking on my Intuitive Eating Journey, I began working with a Life Coach. I started noticing how the Principles of Intuitive Eating related to other areas of my life. Giving myself permission to eat all food was helping me give myself permission to be all the parts of me. With the guidance of my Life Coach, I began to see how Intuitive Eating was a way to unlock what I really wanted— **Intuitive Living.**

Intuitive Living

Intuitive Eating

That's my new RelationSHIP with food!

Unconditional Permission-granting

can extend far beyond the reaches of FOOD.

My Relationship with food Mirrors my Relationship with Life, so if I find myself restricting around food, I am most likely limiting myself in other areas as well.

Congratulations!

You have hereby been appointed Principal of this human body Academy, Ultimate Giver of Hall Passes, Writer of Rules, Maker of Exceptions-to-the-Rules. Exercise your CEO-Level power by writing yourself the exact Permission Slip(s) you've been dying to Receive...

As the Badass Boss of this Establishment, I hereby grant

_____
(your name here)

unconditional permission to be exactly who they are, exactly where they are in THIS moment and in all additional moments to come.

_____   _____
Your Signature   The Universe

What if I don't know which parts of me need more permission to exist?

You can start by getting curious about your **SECRET thoughts!**

What secret thoughts am I afraid to admit to myself?

Secret Thoughts?! They are secret for a reason! Thinking them will be painful!

But since I'm just a cartoon, I suppose I can experiment with what feels true, knowing I always have permission to change my mind.

I might not be as satisfied with my life and career as I say I am.

I have a feeling I'm not even coming close to "fulfilling my potential."

But I hate writing that because it means I'm going to have to do something about it. The thought of discovering my life's purpose & daring to live in alignment with it feels too big and too hard. I want to stay comfy and safe.

Oh! Okay! I see the part of myself I've been rejecting—the part that needs love & permission to be here: The part that DOESN'T want to DO THIS! I don't want to do hard things. I don't want to "work on myself." I want to crawl back into a womb-like cave and eat plates of microwaved nachos until I can't feel my tongue.

Discovering the parts of myself I was judging or rejecting showed me where I could give myself more room to exist. I began writing myself permission slips like they were signed blank checks from the Universe...

This certifies that
Katie Barbaro
_____
(your name)

has permission to sit in bed and eat plates of microwaved nachos until they can't feel their tongue.

_____   _____
Your signature   The Universe

Giving myself permission often removed the CHARGE around forbidden foods & behaviors... so I didn't have to act them out.

This certifies that

_____
(your name)

has permission to change their mind & do things in a new way whenever they see fit.

_____   _____
Your signature   The Universe

This certifies that

_____
(your name)

has permission to feel
insecure and afraid of the
unknown.

_____   _The Universe_
your signature   The Universe

This certifies that

_____
(your Name)

has permission to feel Like
the super confident badass
powerhouse they are.

_____   _The Universe_
your Signature   The Universe

This certifies that

_____
(your name)

has unconditional permission
to stop "working on
themselves"— and STOP
weighing themselves while
they're at it.

_____   _The Universe_
your signature   The Universe

Getting Curious...

Warm Lighting, especially twinkle Lights

Dancing along with flocks of birds

Apples dipped in Peanut Butter

Dirty chai Lattes

Things I actually Like

deep teal

Poached eggs on sourdough toast

Overnight Oats w/ chia seeds, dates, almond milk, cinnamon

Roasted veggies: especially sweet potatoes

Sunsets with great clouds

Drawing my feelings

People who speak their truth.

"Sandalwood" apparently

Anything with cinnamon

As I began to discover my preferences around food, **I** noticed that I was out of touch with my preferences in other areas — What **IS** my favorite color? What do I Like to do on weekends now that I'm not compulsively over-exercising to make up for what I ate the night before? What is my favorite neighborhood? My favorite coffee shop? My favorite thing to do in that coffee shop?

Paying attention to what tickles my fancy makes Life feel more fanciful ♡

Just as Significant:

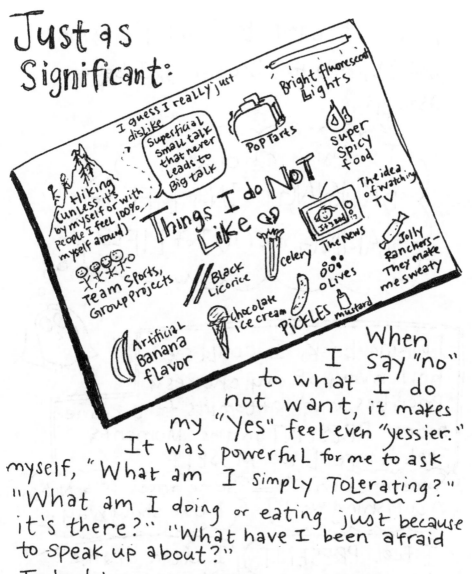

I guess I really just dislike

Superficial small talk that never leads to Big talk

Bright fluorescent Lights

Pop Tarts

super spicy food

Hiking (unless it's with by myself or with people I feel 100% myself around)

The idea of watching TV

Things I do NOT Like

Team Sports, Group Projects

Black Licorice

Celery

The News

Olives

Jolly Ranchers — They make me sweaty

Chocolate ice cream

PICKLES

mustard

Artificial Banana flavor

When I say "no" to what I do not want, it makes my "Yes" feel even "yessier." It was powerful for me to ask myself, "What am I simply Tolerating?" "What am I doing or eating just because it's there?" "What have I been afraid to speak up about?"

I had been operating under the assumption that my dislikes were something to hide — to the point I was hiding them even from myself. While I didn't want to form an identity around complaining, NOTICING what I do not prefer is just as interesting as noticing what I do prefer. Getting curious about myself like this often led to my best standup material — a fun bonus!

When it came to Food Decisions (and BEYOND Food Decisions), I began asking:

Is this choice BRINGING me INto LIFE or TAKING me OUT of LIFE?

Looking back, I could see how many of my choices & priorities were attempts to become more PRESENT in the Moment & feel more like MYSELF.

Sometimes in a nourishing way:

Sometimes in a Not-so-Nourishing way:

I feel PRESENT when I'm performing on stage, Hosting Brunch for friends, writing what feels true to me.

I often drank alcohol to feel permission to be fun, uninhibited ME! Bingeing & Purging violently pulled me into the present moment.

Many Roads Lead to PRESENCE

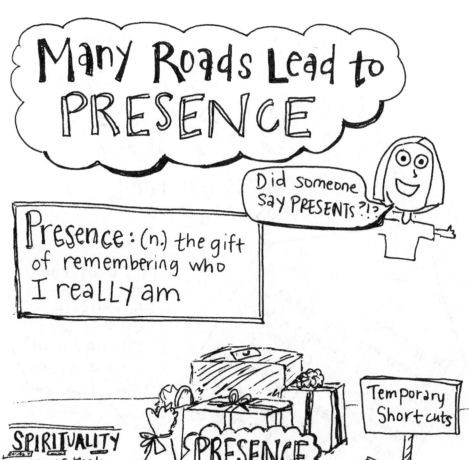

Presence: (n.) the gift of remembering who I really am

Did someone say PRESENTS?!?

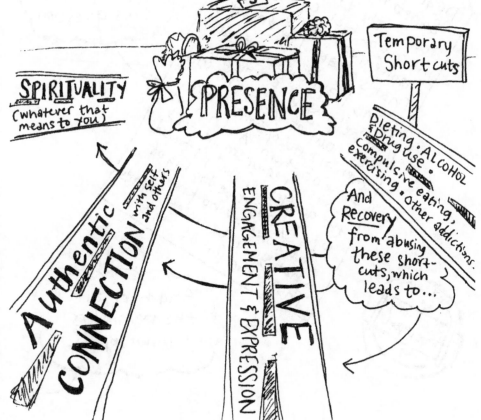

PRESENCE

Temporary Short cuts

SPIRITUALITY (whatever that means to you)

Authentic CONNECTION with self and others

CREATIVE ENGAGEMENT & EXPRESSION

Dieting · ALCOHOL & Drug use · compulsive eating · exercising · other addictions.

And Recovery from abusing these short-cuts, which leads to...

Unwrapping Presence:

What makes me feel the most "ME"?

Dear Katie,

Sometimes you forget about the things that make you feel curious, inspired, and delighted. That's okay! I'm enclosing some happiness reminders to help you if you ever feel out of ideas. This isn't even all the options, only some of them. And none of this is a requirement—it's the gentlest of nudges towards "joy." Joy might be too big of a word even. Who knows what you'll be nudged towards! That's the fun of it. ♥

Here is the note I wrote to myself when I was asking myself this question.

MAY 2017
Recovery Time Capsule

And here are the reminders I unwrapped...

use your hands.

to write. to draw. to build. to make a cool thing. to touch things. to put your vision into the physical world.

dance.

in a class. alone in the apartment. with a stranger. embrace your silliness.

♡♡♡

nourish

your friendships.

call old friends. make new friends. connect with others. open your heart.

♡♡♡

yourself

Eat food that tastes good. move in gentle, rejuvenating ways. drink plenty of water every day. sleep. meditate. avoid caffeine. walk in the park. Kayak on the Hudson. Buy fresh veggies. Read good books. Listen to music that moves you.

paint ♡

you always have the impulse to do this — do it more so you don't build it up to be some "special occasion" thing.

Share

your voice

write. blog. click "publish"

sing

I know you're scared to do this and to admit you like doing it. Just sing by yourself! Share when you feel brave. Create music with your body and voice. It's what your heart wants. You can do it everyday.

say no

to things you don't really want to do. If you're not sure, **pause** and ask. ♡

You don't need anyone to tell you what you're doing is **Right**.

follow the impulse and move ♡

SIMPLY BEING ALIVE ON THIS PLANET IS THE ONLY PERMISSION you need to CREATE ♡

BE where you ARE ♡

My goal is to be able to confidently answer the question "What are your goals?"

September 12, 2017 ♡

Cultivating trust with myself is a worthwhile venture. It may take time, money, pain, patience, and more effort than it seems like it should—know that it's worth it. You are worth it. As soon as you try putting yourself in a box, you've lost touch with the ever-changing, developing, growing parts of yourself. How can you honor yourself for all that you are? Love yourself for everything you are now and everything you will become. Have fewer expectations of yourself to change along pre-determined lines. Give yourself permission to grow and change unexpectedly. It is impossible to lose yourself. You have been and will always be

Right here ♡

My Life Coach helped me sift through the values I was living by and recognize which ones actually belonged to me and which were vestiges of a life I thought I "should" be living. It was groundbreaking to realize I could live a life completely based on my own values — fill up my days with things that make me feel like Me ♡

Before intentionaLLy naming my vaLues, I had some fleeting experiences of feeLing IN ALignment with my soul but had no idea why. Sifting through the golden nuggets of my values gave me the raw material to Lay the foundation for my whole Life ♡

SAFETY: FeeLing At HOME in my BODY & Environment

CHALLENGE: PLacing myself in an atmosphere of GROWTH

Playful CHILDLIKE LAUGHTER♡

COURAGEOUS VULNERability

Accountable IntelLigence AKA INTEgrity

Expansion

CONNECTION with MYSELF, OTHERS & A Higher Power ♡

CReative CURiOSity & EX-PRESS-ION ☆

Authentic Honesty

Kindness

Discovering my True Values was not about Looking externally, but Noticing what consistently mattered to me despite the ever-fluctuating circumstances of my life.

What has remained TRUE for me, even when my life has changed?

Mary Catherine Bateson writes in her book Composing a Life: "If your opinions and commitments appear to change from year to year or decade to decade, what are the more abstract underlying convictions that have held steady, that might never have become visible without the surface variation?"

First I was a highly obedient Catholic school girl Valedictorian, then I was an agnostic standup comedian who told jokes about my catholic upbringing, and write RIGHT now I'm drawing this cartoon in a book about how my relationship with a Higher Power helped me recover from food & body obsession. It's safe to say I value discovering the most true truth I can access. Maybe my next book will be about aliens.

Now that I know my values, what would I LOVE to do next? What is the direction of my highest excitement? What would make me wake up with the feeling "OMG— I GET to be ME!"?

After many long nights of soul searching & realizing Stand Up was no longer lighting my fire like it once had, I was walking alone on the Lower East Side of Manhattan & it came to me:

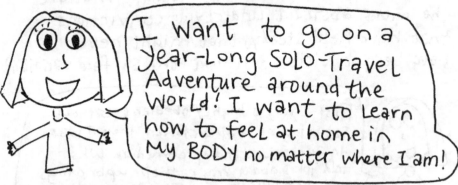

I want to go on a year-long SOLO-Travel Adventure around the world! I want to learn how to feel at home in My BODY no matter where I am!

The CLARITY that Traveling was my Next Step came as a rush of Tingly excitement coursing through my veins. (Honestly, I thought I'd be writing a Book about that right now, but this one wanted to come out first. I'm not in charge!)

Chapter 9
Creativity Picnic

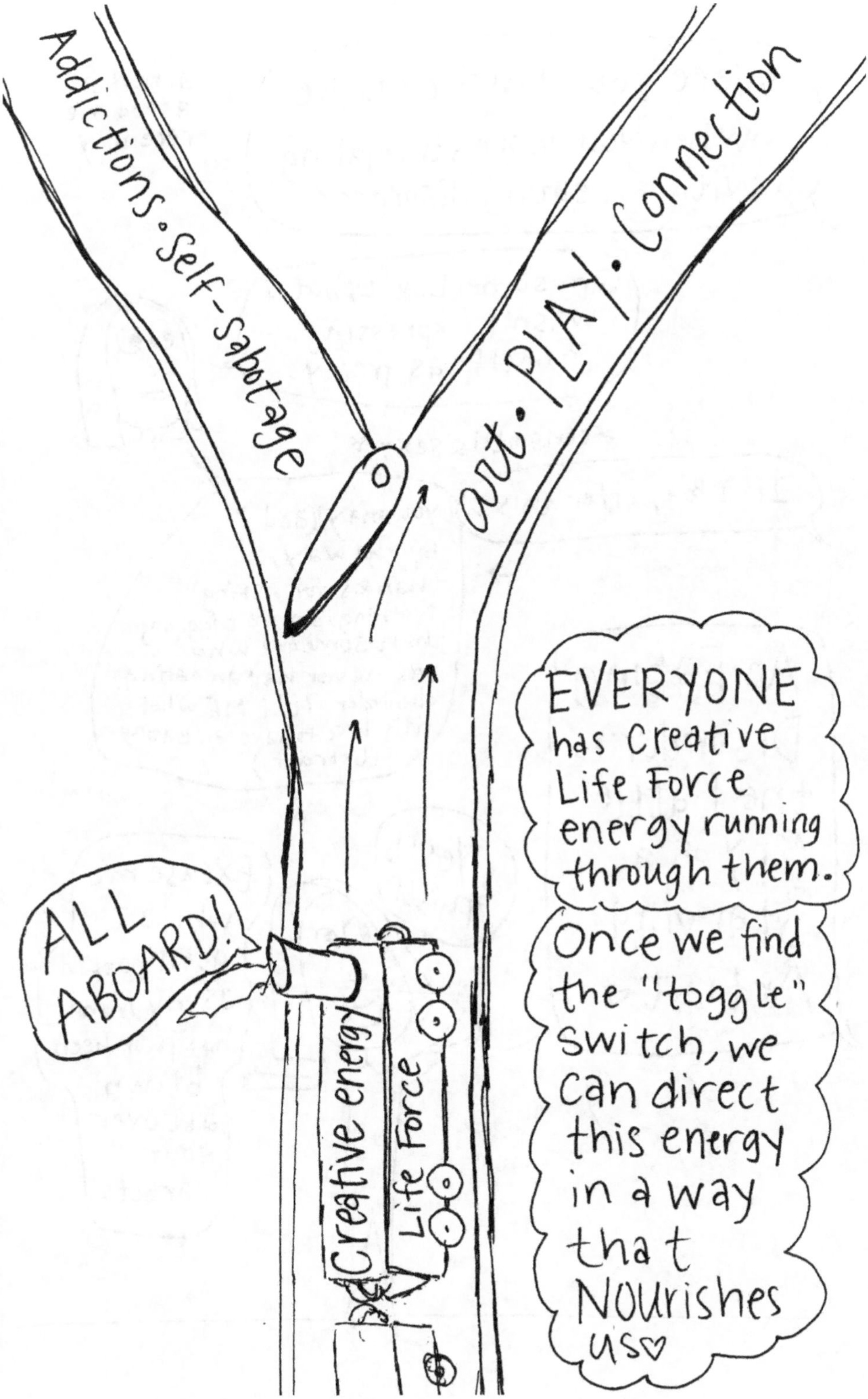

Addictions · Self-Sabotage

art · PLAY · Connection

ALL ABOARD!

Creative energy

Life Force

EVERYONE has Creative Life Force energy running through them.

Once we find the "toggle" switch, we can direct this energy in a way that NOURISHES us♡

Creative Expression

has not only been a RESULT of my Healing Journey, but it has also been a

Catalyst for it ♡

You've probably noticed by now that Writing & drawing help me process MY Sticky Secret Thoughts & Feelings.

Speaking of **Secret Thoughts**...

I experienced challenging Self-Sabotage & a resurgence of Compulsive eating behaviors WHILE WRITING THIS BOOK. (NOT surprisingly... we really stirred up some STUFF!)

The next several Pages are my ♡ **Real Time Response** ♡ to these challenges.

It doesn't get any hotter off the press than that!

Recovery

is Committing to meeting each new LAYER of my PERSONALITY that arises with COMPASSION & LOVE ♡

As Ram Dass often says, "Yes. And that one too." ...meaning "yes, I accept and love this part of me as well. All is welcome here."

Yes. And that one too ♡

I'm annoyed I still seem to be INCREDIBLY human. I'd prefer to be enlightened already.

♡ Yes. And that one too.

I can't possibly admit any of this in the book I'm writing about "healing your relationship with food." I'll be seen as a FRAUD! A phony!

Yes. And that one too.

I'm even tempted to throw up to make it all "go away."

Yes. And that one too.

I'm disappointed that after all the "work" I've done on myself that I still have moments of struggling with compulsive eating.

Yes. And that one too ♡

I can't believe I just stress-ate 3 bowls of cereal in the middle of the night.

Recovery is

the willingness to meet

discomfort with

curiosity instead of BLAME♥

Hey sweetheart, I noticed you've been thinking about what food you should & shouldn't eat & what your body should & shouldn't look like♥ Your food & body "screentime" is up 50% from last week♥ Is there anything you want to talk about?

Thank you for asking. Sometimes I forget I can just talk to you directly. Part of me thinks I need to act out with food & body obsession to get your attention — or eat until I've been "bad" enough to earn the right to be comforted and held, to have something tangible to commiserate over. I'm afraid of revealing my intangible discomfort because I don't know what's driving it — anger, grief, sadness? A combo of all three? I'm afraid it will consume me. I will lose my me-ness. I will stop loving myself — everyone will stop loving me.

243

No matter what it is, the correct response to any bit of TRUTH I share with myself (or anybody shares with me) is

Thank you♡

Thank who? Thank me? For what?! I'm the one who has succumbed YET AGAIN to the LIES of Diet Culture telling me to blame my body for everything that feels wrong with my life & the best explanation I can come up with is "I'm afraid to feel my anger." Sounds un-helpful to me.

Thank you AGAIN! You are giving me a huge gift every time you reveal more of yourself to me. You are showing me more parts I can Love. Yes, and this one too. You don't need to act out around food to get my attention, but I understand that you do it because you felt like you had to in the past. What could I do to show you I am meeting you with Love every day?♡

A List of Demands

~made on behalf of my sweet little heart~

Ways to make me feel seen, heard & held:

Comfort me with physical touch—massage me with lotion, curl up with me under a cozy blanket, ask me what would feel nourishing for my body & then do that.

Feelings Updates: Ask me how I'm feeling throughout the day & ≡actually≡ listen instead of assuming I'll say the same thing as last time.

Feed me nourishing food that I actually like. Don't get frustrated when I don't know what I like or want— we're both trying our best over here.

Curate an environment that appeals to my senses— rich with smells, sounds, sights, tastes & textures I love♥

Look into my eyes in the mirror. Say "I love you" or "I am willing to love you" until you mean it.

Time OUT (or IN)

Allow me to take as many breaks to reflect and go inward without judging me for "not being productive."

Now about that anger you're (I'm)
afraid to feel... 1. This is a completely
┌──────────────────┐   Normal response based on
│ Instructions from │ → your conditioning. Thank
│ The Universe ♡   │   your brain for behaving exactly
└──────────────────┘ → as it was trained to behave.

2. This response is also NO LONGER NECESSARY
for your Survival, so tell your fear-based,
conditioned brain it can take a nap ♡

3. Not only is your anger OKAY to feel, your repressed
anger is also Where your POWER has been HIDING.
Frightening, I Know, to realize you are EVEN MORE
Powerful than you already are. Not only are you
this powerful, you are also infinitely trustworthy. You
wouldn't be given access to power you couldn't handle.

4. In fact—THIS IS THE KEY to how we
transmute the Systemic oppression of diet culture
into WORLD-CHanging Life Force Energy:

Anger with a drop of Love
becomes Passion

What if I allowed it to simply be enough that I've woken up from the illusion of my self-sabotaging thoughts & behaviors? What if instead of gearing up to once again "fix" myself, I realize I never did anything wrong to begin with and turn my "fixing" energy outward? New Policy:

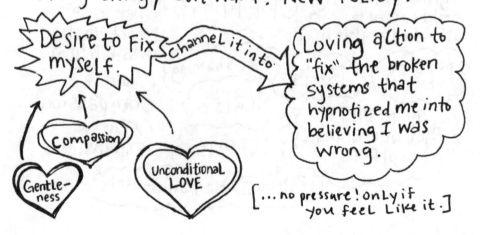

Unlocking the energy stored up in my repressed emotions has felt like a step towards living the empowered, passionate life of my dreams. It's not about becoming Oprah. I want to become ME to the POWER of Oprah.

Here's the math equation:

$$ME^{OPRAH}$$

What do I need to Let Go of to become Myself to the Power of Oprah?

What must I Surrender in order to keep the aliveness of my Recovery?

What can I release to become even more free?

The Desire To Be Perceived as "Right" and "Good"

The Shape & Size of my BODY

PEOPLE-PLEASING

(YES. THIS Needs its own page... maybe its own Book.)

Trying to conceal the Lump in my throat anytime I share my heart authentically with someone else.

The Illusion that I have CONTROL over any of This.

The **Fantasy** that a **Prince** or **Princess charming** will come along and **Rescue** me from my life... *POOF* "Great job with all the 'work' you've done on yourself - Now we can hop on my trusty steed and gallop away into the Sunset together! This is your reward for being such a Good Person!

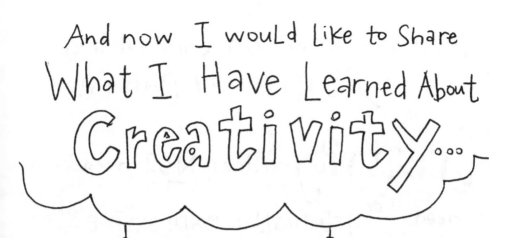

And now I would Like to Share
What I Have Learned About
Creativity...

I'm not trying to CONVINCE
you to Be Creative;
I'm here to REMIND you
that YOU ALREADY ARE.

No way, I'm not Creating anything! I just wake up and go through the motions every day to get by & survive. Nothing new, exciting or creative ever happens for me.

THAT! THAT is what you're creating.

Every human on this planet is **Creative** by nature.

"Creativity" does <u>NOT</u> need to mean "artistically expressive."

There is creativity in the way we make each movement of our days, in the ways we...

Raise our kids

Problem-solve at work

Cook our meals

Choose our Outfits

Select Books to read

← you're being creative Right <u>NOW</u>!

Life is a **creative** act.

We are either **aware** of our creative abilities or not ♡

Birth Certificate

This certifies that _____

was born on this ____ day of _____, ____

into a human body on planet earth
and is hereby a co-creator of reality
with the universe. They are welcome to
explore and express any and all aspects
of the human experience while they're here.

The Universe

_____   _____
witness   The Universe

Friendy Reminder: YOU CANNOT
MESS THIS UP. Your life — exactly
as it is — down to the tiniest & most
"regrettable" details — is PERFECT.
Every time you think you've
messed something up, it has
always been another vital
turn in the story arc of your
life. You are exactly where
you are meant to be and you
have all the raw materials you
need to continue creating the
riveting work of art you are ♡

Creativity happens when we fully acknowledge & embrace what is present HERE & NOW.

...so I will take a moment to do that NOW as I write...

I've told myself this is the *LAST* chapter of my book and I feel afraid it won't be good enough.

I can't talk about creativity without also talking about RESISTANCE to creativity. Resistance can look like FULL-BLOWN Eating Disorder-Level Self-Sabotage or a nagging voice in my head saying "You have no right to write!" "Keep your mouth shut!" "You aren't healed enough to share your story!" "Learn how to draw before you ILLUSTRATE A BOOK!"

This Chapter is all about taking the pent-up energy that has previously been given to food & body obsession (or any form of resistance) and RESTORING it to it's true ESSENCE: Creative Life Force Energy. There's no pressure to "be creative"– rather REMOVE the pressure and pay attention to where our energy wants to flow.

In her brilliant & inspiring creativity manifesto "Big Magic", Elizabeth Gilbert recommends talking to fear & resistance. (I recommend this too, along with reading her book! Do yourself a favor & go buy it right now! Get "The Artist's Way" by Julia Cameron too while you're at it! (It's not just for Artists!))

Here's how one of my conversations with Resistance went: (I wrote this out & hung it next to my workspace)

Oh HELLO Resistance! How can I help you?

PLEASE Listen to my very good points about why you are not qualified to be writing a book about your own life and experiences.

Sure thing! Here's a whole page just for you! Air your grievances & worries!

Okay well to start...what if you don't have a good enough Anti-Diet, Intuitive Eating, Health at Every Size perspective & your book is demonized in those circles?! Christy Harrison will never even consider writing a Forward for your book!

♡ Thank you for sharing. I hear you. ♡ Remember our priority is to simply share our truth as authentically as possible and trust it will resonate with whomever it is meant to resonate. Doing this to be accepted by the Anti-Diet movement is not the point. This isn't about belonging to a group or ideology. It's about belonging to yourself. ♡

Creativity

is never about FORCING
or BULLYING ourselves into
"being creative." It is
about NOTICING what is
already here — LISTENING
and RESPONDING ♡

Creativity is our Responsibility:
our ability to respond to life.

Hey, why do
you sit in
your room
and draw
cartoons
all day?

It's my
responsibility
... are we
the same
person?

The <u>way</u> we respond (art, movement,
speaking, problem-solving, etc.) is not as
important as the fact that we <u>are</u> responding.

Ways I've Given Myself Permission to Let my Creativity *flow*

writing "Morning Pages"— 3 pages of stream of consciousness every morning to get all of the gunk & stuck out of my head. This is a tool from "The Artist's Way" by Julia Cameron.

"Doing" The Artist's Way with an accountability buddy.

Signing up for a stand up comedy class!

This is how I really feel.

Sharing my Truth more authentically with friends

Inktober

Committing to a daily drawing challenge on Instagram

Buying the cheapest guitar on Amazon and SLOWLY, quietly, secretly, when I was all alone began singing, letting my voice be heard even if it was just by me.

Dancing, coloring, talking to myself, talking to strangers, traveling SOLO for a year with no "plans," doing what feels fun & expansive without attachment to the outcome.

Welcome to [The Last Page] of the Book!

This Page is the reason I haven't finished many projects — I've held back sharing myself, worried I don't have a good enough ending. But the truth is, THAT'S NOT MY JOB. It's not my job to make Life sound good or to hit a certain number on the scale or to eat & exercise in a way that will make people like me. My job is to show up, be the me-est me I can be, and do my best to tell the Truth about it. I hope that bits of my story help you on your journey of becoming the you-est YOU you can be, that tasting my recipes might inspire you to create more of your own. (← NO pressure!) May we all be Fed Up with that which depletes us, dims our sparkles, makes us small and Fed :BY: that which nourishes us, Lights our Fire, makes us come alive. On behalf of all of us, THANK YOU for BEING HERE ♡

♡ Acknowledgments ♡

Thank you to all of the people who have supported my recovery, loved me unconditionally, and encouraged me to create this book♡ Here is a non-exhaustive cloud collage of beings I'm bursting with gratitude for:

Bruno & Maggie Barbaro (AKA The Best Parents Ever Invented)

Bruno Barbaro Jr.

Phil Wells

Carole Wells

Amber Donebauer

Sammi Travis

Helen Wildy

MYQ Kaplan

Sarah Schultz

Devin Wilson

Joshua Pánczer♡

Kai Mata

Brittany Brave

Eric Paton

Michelle DeBoever

Nassybah Cruz

Liz Glazer

Lyssa Mandel & Writing Church

Hilmar & Jolanta

Rebekah Nanfria

Matt Kahn

Julia Cameron

Everyone I've ever been in a meeting with♡

Christy Harrison

Brené Brown

Elizabeth Gilbert

Glennon Doyle

Ram Dass

Everyone I've ever performed with or for♡

My past & present families at CSz, CDK, USC, DOz, OA... all the Acronyms & forms of families

YOU! Seriously. Thank you for being here with me.
♡

Books I've Referred to
(and a few BONUS books I LOVE)

WOMEN, FOOD, and GOD BY GENEEN ROTH ♥

ANTI-DIET By Christy Harrison, MPH, RD

Health at EVERY Size By Lindo Bacon, Ph.D

The Gifts of Imperfection By Brené Brown, Ph.D, L.M.S.W.

When Things Fall Apart BY PEMA CHODRON

The Power of NOW By Eckhart Tolle

♥ LOVE WARRIOR ♥ BY GLENNON DOYLE

UNTAMED ALSO BY GLENNON DOYLE ♥

The Artist's Way By Julia Cameron

RECOVERY By Russell Brand

BIG MAGIC BY ELIZABETH GILBERT ♥

Intuitive Eating By Evelyn Tribole, MS, RDN, CEDRD-S and ELYSE RESCH, MS, RDN, CEDRD-S, FAND

♡ Resources ♡

If you are feeling weird about your
relationship with food, struggling
with disordered eating, or desiring
more support for your mental wellbeing,
YOU ARE NOT ALONE♡ Here is a list
of resources that can help (or help you find help):

- National Eating Disorders Association (USA)
  ♡ NationalEatingDisorders.org
  ♡ Helpline: 1-800-931-2237
    OR Text "NEDA" to 741741

- Eating Disorder Hope.com

- International Association for Suicide Prevention:
  ♡ IASP.info

- National Suicide Prevention Lifeline (USA)
  ♡ 1-800-273-8255

- Dietitians, Doctors & Therapists with an
  Intuitive Eating & Health at Every Size lens.
  Here's a list of practitioners certified in IE:
  ♡ intuitiveeating.org/certified-counselors
  ♡

It takes strength & courage to ASK for HELP♡

7